BIOGRAPHY OF
PERCIVAL LOWELL

THE MACMILLAN COMPANY
NEW YORK · BOSTON · CHICAGO · DALLAS
ATLANTA · SAN FRANCISCO

MACMILLAN & CO., Limited
LONDON · BOMBAY · CALCUTTA
MELBOURNE

**THE MACMILLAN COMPANY
OF CANADA, Limited**
TORONTO

PERCIVAL LOWELL AGE 61

From a silver point portrait begun before his death and finished afterwards
by Eccolo Cartollo

BIOGRAPHY OF PERCIVAL LOWELL

By

A. LAWRENCE LOWELL

NEW YORK

THE MACMILLAN COMPANY

1935

PRINTED IN THE UNITED STATES OF AMERICA
NORWOOD PRESS LINOTYPE, INC.
NORWOOD, MASS., U.S.A.

PREFACE

IF genius is the capacity for taking infinite pains, Percival Lowell possessed it abundantly from his study of Esoteric Shinto, in his earlier life in Japan, to his great calculation of the position and orbit of an unknown planet beyond Neptune, at the close of his life. In determining facts he was thoroughly and rigidly scientific, leaving nothing unexplored that bore upon the subject; and in his astronomical investigations it became clear to him that better methods of doing it were required. At the outset, therefore, he set up his Observatory in an atmosphere steadier than that where the older telescopes, and almost all of those then in existence, did their work; thus seeing much not visible elsewhere.

But in addition to industry he had an inflammable intellect, easily ignited by any suggestion or observation, and when alight glowing in intensity until the work was done. He had also a highly vivid imagination, compared with many men of science who proceeded more cautiously; and hence he sought, not only to ascertain new facts, but to draw conclusions from them more freely than is customary with experts of that type. This he felt had often been true of those who made advances in scientific thought, and he regarded himself as standing for a time somewhat apart from most men in his own field. Such an attitude, and the fact that he had taken up observational astronomy in middle life, unconnected with any other scientific institution, tended to make many professional astronomers look upon him askance. So he plowed his own furrow largely by himself in the spirit of a pioneer, and this little volume is an attempt to tell what he accomplished.

The writer is very grateful to the Houghton, Mifflin Company, the Macmillan Company, The Atlantic Monthly, Rhodora, the Scientific American, and Miss Katharine G. Macartney (on behalf of Mrs. George Gould) for permission to quote, sometimes at great length, from books and articles by and about Percival. The writer desires also to express his deep obligation to Mr. George R. Agassiz, his brother's intimate friend and helper, to Dr. Vesto Melvin Slipher, Dr. Carl O. Lampland and Mr. E. C. Slipher of the Lowell Observatory at Flagstaff, for reading the manuscrapt and giving advice; and to Professor Henry Norris Russell of Princeton University, for his kindness in not only doing this, but for writing the two appendices that follow this volume. Without their help the astronomical part of this book would have been sadly defective. They have pointed out advances in knowledge that have made certain of Percival's opinions, particularly earlier ones, no longer tenable. Some of these he changed during his lifetime, others he would have changed had he lived to see the more ample facts since known. Nor is this a criticism of his work, for astronomy has been advancing rapidly of late; and when that is true no man can expect all his views, even if accepted at the time, to endure. Change in opinions is the penalty of growing knowledge. It is enough that a man has helped to push knowledge and thought forward while he lived, and this Percival, with the exhaustless energy of his nature, certainly did.

Boston, October 21, 1935.

CONTENTS

ILLUSTRATIONS

BIOGRAPHY OF
PERCIVAL LOWELL

CHAPTER I

CHILDHOOD AND YOUTH

THE particular assortment of qualities a man inherits, from among the miscellaneous lot his ancestors no doubt possessed and might have transmitted, is of primary importance to him. In this Percival Lowell was fortunate. From his father's family he derived a very quick apprehension, a capacity for intellectual interests, keen and diversified, and a tireless joy in hard mental labor; while from his mother's people he drew sociability, ease of companionship and charm; from both families a scorn of anything mean or unworthy, a business ability and the physical health that comes from right living. His life is the story of the use he made of these heirlooms.

The son of Augustus Lowell and Katharine Bigelow (Lawrence), Percival Lowell was born in Boston on March 13, 1855, at 131 Tremont Street where the Shepard stores now stand. The region was then residential, and his parents went there so that his mother might be near her father, the Hon. Abbott Lawrence, whose house was on Park Street, now the main portion of the Union Club. He had fallen ill since his return as Minister to England, and was now failing fast. Percival was her first-born, but others followed rapidly, involving removal to larger quarters; first to Park Square, and then to 81 Mount Vernon Street, where

even the games of little boys were tinged by the overshadow-
ing events of the day,—the drilling and the battles of the
Civil War. He went to a dame school kept by Miss Fette;
and being always a good scholar learned what he should; for
he developed normally. After infancy the summer was
spent at Beverly in the pleasures and occupations of early
childhood.

But in the spring of 1864 there came a sudden change.
His mother was far from well, and losing ground so fast
that his father was advised to take her abroad for a complete change as her only chance,—a heroic remedy which
proved in time successful. So the family sailed in the *Africa,*
a paddle-wheel steamer of 2500 tons with the sails of a full-
rigged ship,—the father with an invalid wife, four children
aged from nine to two, a nurse sea-sick all the time; and in
addition the care of three more children of a friend in
Europe, with a nurse who was well, but bereft of sense.
However, they arrived safely, spent the summer in England,
and, as all Americans did in those days, went to Paris for
the winter.

Here Percival began a life different from that of his con-
temporaries at home; for with his younger brother and his
cousin, George P. Gardner,—one of the children who had
crossed with him on the *Africa*—he went to a French boarding school kept by a Mr. Kornemann. We were allowed to
come home for Sundays, but spent the rest of the week at
the school,—a very wise arrangement; for, although there
were some English boys, the atmosphere was French, and
we learned the language easily, by the native method of
teaching it. To Percival this was a great benefit throughout
his life.

Two winters were spent in this way, the intervening summer being passed by the family in travel. In the spring of 1866 his parents proposed to go for a few weeks to Italy, and take the children with them; but Percival was so ill at ease in travel that he was left at the famous boarding school kept by the Silligs at Vevey. Although in mature life a constant traveller, this event was not out of character, for not being yet old enough to enjoy the results of travel, or feel the keen interest in them later aroused, he was too restless to find pleasure in long journeying without an object. On their return from Italy the family picked him up and went to Germany, where they were caught by the seven weeks' war with Austria. When it broke out they were at Schwalbach in Nassau, one of the smaller states that took sides against Prussia. Percival always remembered vividly what he there saw, exciting enough for a small boy; the sudden clatter of a galloping horse, as a man in civilian dress passed the hotel up a small lane to the left. It was the burgomaster carrying word of Prussian advance, followed quickly by the sound of several more horses, and three videttes in blue galloped past, turning up the main road in front of the hotel where they supposed the burgomaster had gone. Up the road they went and disappeared round a turn to the left at the top of the slope. Scarcely had they vanished when a squad of green-clad Nassau infantry appeared, and following half-way up the hill hid behind a wood pile. It was not long before the Prussian videttes, having failed to find the burgomaster, came into sight again, leisurely walking their horses down the road. When abreast of the wood pile the Nassau squad stole out, firing from the hip in the manner of the day. Whether they hit anyone we never knew, but the enemy was wholly dispersed, for one of the horsemen wheeled up the hill, another spurred his horse down past the hotel, and the third jumped his over the wall into the garden of the baths. That afternoon a Nassau regiment marched into the town and bivouacked in the streets, leaving in the morning to be replaced later in the day by a Prussian regiment, which in its turn marched off to its rendezvous near Kissingen.

By the end of the summer of 1866 Mother was well enough to go home, and the whole family sailed for Boston. Percival's education there was of the ordinary classical type preparatory for college, for one year at a school kept by a Mr. Fette, brother of his teacher in childhood, and then for five years in that of Mr. George W. C. Noble, whose influence, both by teaching and character, was strong with all boys capable of profiting thereby. Percival was always near the top of his class, especially in the Classics, which he acquired so easily that while playing with a toy boat, in a shallow pond made by the melting snow on the lawn at Brookline, it occurred to him to describe an imaginary shipwreck thereof; and he did so in some hundreds of Latin hexameter verses.

In the spring of 1867 Father bought the place at the corner of Heath and Warren Streets in Brookline, where he lived until his death in 1900; and where his last child, Amy, passed her whole life. Here Percival spent his boyhood, summer and winter, until he went to college, enjoying the life and sports of the seasons; and, in fact, he was a normal boy like his comrades, only more so. During the earlier years Father drove us into town and out again each day, he going to his office and the children to school. On the

PERCIVAL LOWELL
And His Biographer

road he talked on all subjects and we learned much in this way. Somehow he made us feel that every self-respecting man must work at something that is worth while, and do it very hard. In our case it need not be remunerative, for he had enough to provide for that; but it must be of real significance. I do not know that he ever said this formally, but, by the tenor of his conversation and his own attitude toward life, he impressed that conviction deeply upon the spirit. From his own active and ambitious nature, Percival little required such a stimulus; and, indeed, he struck out an intellectual path of his own in boyhood. He took to astronomy, read many books thereon, had a telescope of his own, of about two and a quarter inches in diameter, with which he observed the stars from the flat roof of our house; and later in life he recalled that with it he had seen the white snow cap on the pole of Mars crowning a globe spread with blue-green patches on an orange ground. This interest he never lost, and after lying half-dormant for many years it blazed forth again as the dominant one in his life, and the field of his remarkable achievements.

The two years of school in Paris certainly had not retarded his progress, if, indeed, the better European discipline had not advanced it; for he could have been prepared for college at sixteen, but it was thought well to extend the time another year and fill in with other things. Strangely enough, Mr. Noble thought him not so strong as he might be in two subjects where he later excelled,—English Composition and Mathematics,—and in these he was tutored the year before entering college. Later he thought he had been misjudged, but one may suspect it was rather because his interest in these matters had not been aroused. The capacity was there but not yet awakened. However, he entered college in the autumn of 1872 not only clear but with honors in Mathematics. In fact he studied that subject every year in college, took second-year honors in it, and Professor Benjamin Peirce, the great mathematician, spoke of him as one of the most brilliant scholars ever under his observation, hinting to him that if he would devote himself thereto he could succeed him in his chair. Yet it was by no means his sole field of knowledge, for he elected courses also in the Classics, Physics and History, doing well enough in all of them to be in the ΦBK and have a Commencement part. An impression of his versatility is given by the fact that in his senior year he won a Bowdoin Prize for an essay on "The Rank of England as a European Power from the Death of Elizabeth to the Death of Anne," and spoke his part on "The Nebular Hypothesis."

Yet he was no recluse; for he was constantly that year at dancing parties in Boston; and, being naturally sociable, and strongly attached to his friends, he made many in college. With Harcourt Amory, his Freshman chum, he went abroad, after graduating in 1876, and spent a year in Europe. The young men went to London with letters that brought them into delightful society there, and they travelled over the British Isles and the Continent. It was mainly the *grand tour;* but although he wrote many letters, and kept a journal, these, so far as preserved, reveal little of his personality except a keen joy in natural beauty and a readiness in acquaintance with people casually met. Alone, he went down the Danube, and tried,—fortunately without success,—to get to the front in the war then raging between Servia and Turkey. With Harcourt Amory he went also to Palestine and Syria, at that time less visited than they are to-day; but for this part of his journey, where it would be most interesting, his journal, if written, is lost. His love of travel had fairly begun.

CHAPTER II

FIRST VISIT TO JAPAN

IN the summer of 1877 he came home; and, having no
impulse toward a profession, he went into the office of his
grandfather, John Amory Lowell, where he was engaged in
helping to manage trust funds. In this,—in learning the
ways of business, for a time as acting treasurer, that is the
executive head, of a large cotton mill, and withal as a young
man of fashion,—he spent the next six years. With money
enough for his wants, never extravagant, and with the increase that came from shrewd investment, he felt free in the
spring of 1883 to go to Japan to study the language and the
people. Both of these he did with his habitual energy, learning to speak with great rapidity, meeting socially Japanese
and foreign residents in Tokyo, and observing everything to
be seen. His own view of the value of travel and study is
given in a letter to a sister seven years his junior, written
apparently in the preceding summer when she was in Europe.[1] "I am very glad," he says, "that you are taking so
much interest in studying what you come across in your
journey and after all life itself is but one long journey which
is not only misspent but an unhappy one if one does not
interest one's-self in whatever one encounters—Besides, from

[1] It is dated Boston, August 24th, but the year does not appear. She was
abroad and he at home in the summers of 1882 and 1887.

8

another standpoint, you are storing up for yourself riches
above the reach of fickle fate,—what the moths and rust
of this world cannot touch. You are making, as it were, a
friend of yourself. One to whom you can go when time or
place shall sever you from others, and the older you grow,
sweet puss, the more you have to depend upon yourself. So,
school your mind then, that it may come to the rescue of
your feelings—and a great thing is to cultivate this love of
study while yet you are happy. For if you wait until you
need it to be happy, you will, with much more difficulty,
persuade yourself to forget yourself in it—Now as to par-
ticulars, you need never worry yourself if you do not happen
to like what it is orthodox to prefer. You had much better
be honest with yourself even if wrong, than dishonest in
forcing yourself to agree with the multitude. That is, the
opinion one most commonly hears is not always the opinion
of the best. And again, always be able to give a reason for
what you think and, to a great extent, for what you like."

At once he was fascinated by Japan, its people, their customs, their tea-houses, gardens and their art. Much of this
was more novel to his friends at home when he wrote about
it than it would be now; although even at that time he saw
how much Tokyo had already been influenced by Western
ideas and habits. He kept his attention alert, observing,
studying, pondering everything that he saw or heard. In
fact, within a fortnight he lit upon two things that later led
to careful examination and the writing of books. In a letter
to his mother on June 8, in dealing with differences that
struck him between the people of Japan and occidentals, he
writes: "Again, perhaps, a key to the Japanese is impersonalism. Forced upon one's notice first in their speech, it may

be but the expression of character. In the Japanese language there is no distinction of persons, no sex, no plural even. I speak of course of their inflected speech. They have pronouns, but these are used solely to prevent ambiguity. The same is true of their genders and plurals. To suppose them, however, destitute of feeling, as some have done, I am convinced would be an error. The impersonalism I speak of is a thing of the mind rather than the heart. I suggest rather than posit." In a letter, three days later, he tells of a friend whose jin-riki-sha man's wife had the fox disease, "a species of acute mania supposed by the people to be a bewitchment by the fox. As the person possessed so regards it and others assist in keeping up the delusion by interpreting favorably to their own views, it is no wonder that the superstition survives." Some years later an unexpected sight of a religious trance on Mount Ontake gave rise to a careful study of these psychic phenomena. Well did Pasteur remark that in the fields of observation chance favors only the minds that are prepared.

He hired a house in Tokyo, set up his own establishment as if he had been born and bred there, and after three weeks on shore wrote: "I am beginning to talk Japanese like a native (of America), and I take to ye manners and customs of ye country like a duck to the water." He stayed enjoying the life, and the many friends he made, until the middle of July, when, with Professor Terry of the University, he started on a trip across the mountains to the other side of the island. The journey was hard, and at times the food and lodging poor. "Think," he writes, "of the means of subsistence in a land where there is no milk, no butter, no cheese, no bread, almost no meat, and not over many eggs.

Rice is the staple article of food, then vegetables, eggs and fish; the last two being classed as the food of the richer, and most eaten in the greater centres. Some country people are so poor that they have not rice, and eat barley instead. It is considered a sign of poverty to be without this universal article of diet, but in travelling about in out-of-the-way corners one meets with such places. I have myself lit upon such at the noon-day halt but have never been obliged to spend the night there." But the scenery was fine, and the people unchanged by contact with the foreigner. He noted archaic devices still in use for pumping and boiling water; yet, in visiting a ruined castle, he saw that while the interior of the country had as yet been little affected by the impact of the West its political condition had been transformed with amazing speed. "We mounted through some seven barnlike rooms, up Japanese ladders to the top story. Sitting by the window and looking at the old feudal remains below, the moat with its stagnant slime and the red dragon flies skimming its surface, the old walls, the overgrown ramparts where now the keeper tries to grow a crop of beans, all tended to carry my thoughts back to the middle ages, or was it only to my own boyhood when the name *middle ages* almost stood for fairy land? And yet all this had been a fact, even while I had been dreaming of it. My dreams of Western feudalism had been co-existent with Eastern feudalism itself. So it was only eleven years ago that the last Daimio of the place left the castle of his ancestors forever."

From his journey across Japan he got back to Tokyo on August 13th, where a surprise and an opportunity awaited him. On the very evening of that day he was asked to accompany a Special Mission from Korea to the United States as its Foreign Secretary and Counsellor. About this Dr. W. Sturgis Bigelow wrote to Percival's father:

"After two days of unconditional refusal and one of doubt Percy has finally yielded to the wishes of the U. S. Legation here and accepted the position of Foreign Secretary and General Counsellor to the Embassy sent from Korea to the U. S.

"The position practically amounts to his having complete charge and control of the most important legation from a new country that has visited the U. S. since the opening of Japan. The U. S. authorities here are greatly pleased at having secured so good a man, as is natural. There were many applicants for the place."

He goes on to say the hesitation was mainly due to anxiety to what his father would say, and adds:

"He distrusts himself too much, he has great ability, he has learned Japanese faster than I ever saw any man learn a language —and he only needs to be assured that he is doing the right thing to make a success of anything he undertakes, whether science or diplomacy."

CHAPTER III

KOREA

It was the first diplomatic mission from the hermit kingdom to any Western power, and they wanted someone with *savoir faire* to look after them. He accepted the post, landing in San Francisco with his charges on September 2nd, and crossing to New York, where the Embassy was received by President Arthur. After spending six weeks in the United States he returned by the Pacific with the greater part of his colleagues, reaching Japan in November. They felt grateful for what he had done, and he was invited to go on with them to Korea as the guest of the King—a chance not to be lost, so he went, and after sundry wearisome delays in transit came to Söul, the capital of the Kingdom, just before Christmas, 1883.

Evidently he had not intended so long a sojourn and study as he was destined to make, for in a letter to his mother on December the 20th, just after landing at Chemulpo, the port of Söul, he writes: "I purpose to study the land a little and then return overland either to Pusan" (the Japanese treaty port at the extreme southern end of the peninsula) "or after some travelling in the interior here, Gensan." He had as yet no idea of the impossibility of travel in Korea in the winter, especially for an occidental, but he learned it the following day when with much discomfort he went half way to

13

Söul, the whole distance from the port to the capital being twenty-seven miles. Another and stronger reason for his prolonged stay was the hospitality tendered and the solicitude for his comfort. At Nagasaki, where the ship stopped on the journey from Japan, his Korean colleagues, observing his preference, engaged a Japanese familiar with European cooking to become a member of his household, and they brought along also chairs for his use. In the letter to his mother just quoted he writes; "I think I shall either take a house of my own or, perhaps better, have a part of a Corean's to my exclusive use. . . . I shall of course be asked to stay at our minister Foote's, but I shall fight shy of it in order to be less tied politically.[1] You see there are national parties even in this small state, and I think it best for me to be, at any rate at first, on the cross benches. Out in the Far East the ministers of foreign countries are always mixed up in national politics, and Corea is no exception to the rule." A shrewd observation in view of the fact that hardly a year passed before there was bloodshed between the adherents of China and Japan in the government, when the Japanese legation was attacked and fought its way to the sea.

He found that there had been prepared for him a house, or rather group of buildings forming a part of the Foreign Office, of which he was formally a member as having been Counsellor to the Embassy to America. "From the street," he writes, "you enter a courtyard, then another, then a garden, and so on, wall after wall, until you have left the outside world far behind and are in a labyrinth of your own. Before you lies a garden; behind another surrounded by porticoes. Courtyards, gardens, porticoes, rooms,

---

[1] Before leaving Korea he spent two delightful weeks at the Footes.

corridors in endless succession until you lose yourself in the delightful maze." He speaks of the painting of landscapes on the walls, of a door cut out as a circle in the wall into which fit two sliding panels beautifully painted on both sides. "Floor, ceiling, walls all are paper. But you would hardly imagine that what you tread upon, to all appearance square stone slabs, is oil paper so hard as even in sounds under your footfalls to resemble flags. . . . Through the thick sliding windows sifts the golden light into the room, and for the nonce you forget that outside is the dull grey of a cloudy sky and a snow decked land of a December afternoon."

There he spent the winter under strangely favorable conditions; one of the first men of European race to enter the country with an official position and no official duties or restraints, and a couple of officers detailed to care for him, without hampering him by constant attendance on his movements. In fact he seems to have been more free than anyone in the land. It was beneath the dignity of a higher official to go through the streets except in a palanquin; and all others, save blind men, must not be out of their houses after night-fall on pain of flogging. But finding that to be carried squatting on the cold floor of a box two and a half feet square was intolerable, he took to his feet; and, being an official, he walked all over the city at any hour of the day or night, without this foreign eccentricity shocking either the high or the lowly. He was received in special audience by the King and the Crown Prince, and later photographed them; was visited and entertained abundantly, made many acquaintances and some warm friends. On February 2nd, he wrote to his mother: "I think it will please your maternal ear to hear of the esteem in which your boy is held and of the honors and great kindness which are lavished upon him. On New Year's.Eve [2] he received some gifts from the King, made on purpose for him, a description of which you will find in a letter to Katie. They were accompanied by the wish on the part of His Majesty 'that in view of my speedy return, he hoped that I would come back next year.' I had informed them of my departure before long, which they do not view favorably. I was also told that I was constantly in the King's thoughts. He is hospitality and kindness itself to everyone. I have seen several houses of the highest nobles in the land and there is none to compare with the establishment they have given me. I have been consulted on foreign business, my requests for others granted, talked to on home matters, in short I am looked upon as a friend of the government and cared for in corresponding style."

Delightful as the experience was, there came over him in time a desire to go back to more familiar surroundings, and as spring approached he spoke of his intention. They tried to dissuade him, and did induce him to delay his departure; but at last he sailed with no little feeling of sadness in leaving a country where he had been so kindly treated and which he was never to see again. In a letter to his sister Bessie, on February 17, not long before his departure he wrote: "I have already taken fifty-three negatives of scenes in and about Söul, groups and individuals. I am not only expected by the Coreans but urged to write a book; but as I have a wholesome dread of publication I reserve my decision. I am to send as a present to His Majesty a collection of my photographs printed in Japan on my return."

[2] This came about a month later than ours.

PERCIVAL LOWELL AND THE MEMBERS OF THE KOREAN EMBASSY

CHAPTER IV

HIS FIRST BOOK, "CHOSÖN"

HE did write the book, and published it in 1885, under the title of "Chosön—the Land of the Morning Calm—A Sketch of Korea." It is an account of his personal experiences, under peculiarly favorable conditions, in a land of Asiatic civilization almost wholly unknown to the outer world, and as such it was, and after fifty years remains, a highly interesting book of travel. Although there is too much clever play on words, a natural temptation to a brilliant young writer, the story is graphically told, with much appreciation and many poetic touches on men and scenes. But the book is far more than this. It is a careful study of the land and its people, their customs, ideas and manner of life. He describes the geography of the country and of the walled capital, then little known, the legends and government; the houses and mode of life of the upper and lower classes, then sharply distinguished; the architecture, landscape gardening and costumes, some of them very peculiar; for while much of the civilization had been derived from China, and parts of it bore a close relation to the conditions in Japan, it was in many ways quite distinct and unlike anything else even in the Far East. Three things struck him greatly, as lying at the base of the mode of life, and these he called the triad of principles. They were the strange lack of individual

17

variation, which he called the quality of impersonality, of which we shall hear more in connection with the Japanese; the patriarchal system, with the rules of inheritance and the relation of children to the fathers, which was carried very far; and the position of women, in which the principle of exclusion, universal as it is in Asia, was more rigidly enforced than elsewhere in the Far East.

He was also impressed by the absence of what we understand by religion, in substance or in manifestation, unless the ethics of Confucius can be so called. Save for a few monasteries there were no ecclesiastical buildings, no temples, no services, public or observable. Buddhist priests had long been excluded from the walled cities, and the ancient cult that developed into Shinto in Japan died out or never developed. On the other hand, there was a general belief in a multitude of demons, some good, but, so far as they affected man, evil for the most part, and kept away by trivial devices, like images of beasts on the roofs and wisps of straw over the doors.

How he succeeded in acquiring all the knowledge set forth in the book it is difficult to conceive, for he was there only about two months, came with the slight knowledge of the language he could have picked up from his colleagues on the Mission to America; and there were only two men, it would seem, who could speak both Korean and any European tongue,—one of them a German in the Foreign Office, and the other an English schoolmaster who had been there but a short time. His chief source of information must have come through people who spoke Korean and Japanese, but his own knowledge of the latter was still very limited, for he had spent only a few months in Japan, and his secretary, Tsunejiro Miyaoka, afterward a distinguished lawyer in Tokyo, who knew English, was desperately ill almost all the time he was in Korea. To have absorbed and displayed so clearly all the information in "Chosön" makes that work, if not one of his greatest contributions to knowledge, yet a remarkable feat. Most books of travel are soon superseded, but this one has a distinct permanent value, because the life he portrays, especially that of the upper class, which was almost all connected with the holding of public office, has been swept away, never to reappear, by the conquest and ultimate incorporation of the country by Japan.

CHAPTER V

THE COUP D'ETAT AND THE JAPANESE MARCH
TO THE SEA

ONE more event in Korea interested him deeply, for it meant life or death to some of his nearest native friends, and under the title of "A Korean Coup d'Etat," he gave a graphic account of it in the *Atlantic Monthly* for November 1886. Although not himself present, since it took place in the December after he had left, it was not unconnected with the Mission to America of which he had been a member; for the policy of opening Korea to the world had not met with universal favor among the officials, and all those who had gone on the Mission did not take it very seriously. In fact the two groups rapidly drew apart, one side seeking to extend foreign contacts and the use of foreign methods, the other preparing to resist this. The latter began to strengthen themselves by enrolling what they called a militia,—really a rough body of men devoted to their interests,—until the progressionists, as their opponents were called, saw that they would be crushed unless they struck quickly. Among their leaders was Hong Yŏng Sik, who had been especially attentive to Percival during his stay in Sŏul, and he with his partisans decided to get control of affairs by the method whereby changes of ministry are often effected at a certain stage of political evolution, that is, by removing objectionable ministers both from office and from the world. The occasion selected was a banquet to celebrate the creation of a post office, that institution being regarded as typical of good or evil in foreign habits. The chief victim was wounded but not killed, whereat the progressionist leaders, pretending to be alarmed for the safety of the King, went to the palace and slew such of the leading opponents as they could lay their hands on; but, having no troops, sent in His Majesty's name to ask the Japanese minister for the protection of his force of one hundred and twenty guards. Not suspecting the real nature of the disturbance, he complied, but was soon attacked by a body of six hundred Chinese soldiers, naturally in sympathy with the conservatives, and at their back the Korean militia. For two days the Japanese guards held off the assailants with little loss to themselves compared with that of their foes, until the King placed himself in the hands of the Korean militia, when there was nothing for the Japanese to do but to get back to their legation as best they could. The rest of the tale he felt so much and told so well in the ephemeral form of a magazine article that it is given here in his own words: [1]

Night had already wrapped the city in gloom, as the column defiled from the palace gate into the black and tortuous streets of the town. No resistance was made to their exit, for, under cover of the darkness, the Korean soldiers had all secretly slipped away. A pall-like obscurity and silence had settled over everything. It seemed the spirit of death. The streets of Söul are for the most part hardly more than wide alleys, crooked and forbidding enough in the daytime. Night converts them into long cavernous passages,

[1] (*Atlantic Monthly*, Nov. 1886, "A Korean Coup d'Etat").

devoid of light, like the underground ramifications of some vast cave; for, by a curious curfew law, they are denied any artificial illumination. Through this sombre labyrinth the Japanese column threaded its way, with nothing to light its path but the reflection in the sky of fires in distant parts of the city,—a weird canopy to an inky blackness. Before long, however, even night failed to yield security from man. At the cross-roads and wherever a side-street offered an opportunity for attack were gathered bands of braves, mixed masses of soldiers and populace, who fired upon them or hurled stones, according to the character of the individuals. Still they pushed steadily forward, though utterly uncertain what they might find at their journey's end; for they had not been able to hear from the legation since the attack on the palace, and were in grave fear for its safety. As they came to the top of a bit of rising ground, they made out by the lurid light of the fires their own flag, the red ball on the white field, flying from its flagstaff, and thus learnt for the first time that the buildings were still standing and in Japanese hands. As they neared the legation the crowds increased, but, sweeping them aside, the troops at length reached their destination at eight o'clock at night, having been absent forty-eight hours.

That the legation was yet safe was not due to any neglect or forbearance on the part of the Koreans. From the moment of the attempted assassination of Min Yöng Ik, the city had fallen a prey to disturbances that grew hourly graver and graver in character, and began to be directed more and more against the Japanese merchants and traders scattered through the town. Such of these as took alarm first hastened to the legation for protection. In this way about seventy of them had collected in the buildings, and they, together with the servants and a score of soldiers that had been left there, had successfully defended the place until the return of the troops. For two whole days the little improvised garrison had kept the besiegers at bay.

The legation was safe, but for the rest it was a melancholy tale which the minister and his suite returned to hear. The sullen glow in the heavens, that had served them for torches across the city, came, they learned, from the burning by the infuriated rabble of the homes of their compatriots. But worse than the loss of property had been the loss of life. The hatred of the Japanese, that had lain smouldering for centuries, had at last found a vent. Shortly after the attack on the palace by the Chinese troops, the cry was raised against the Japanese, and a wholesale pillage and massacre of the foreigners began. . . .

The Japanese gone, the progressionist ministers, realizing that they had failed, fled hastily to such concealment as individual ingenuity suggested. . . . One alone remained to die at his post. The account of his death, given by certain private Korean letters, is a tale of as noble an act of heroism as was ever performed.

When it became evident that the Japanese would withdraw, and the progressionist leaders be left to their fate, the latter, perceiving that if they remained they must inevitably fall into the hands of the enemy, prepared for flight. To the surprise and horror of all the others, Hong Yŏng Sik calmly informed them that he should stay. The rest, indeed, had better go, but one, he thought, ought to remain, to show the world that the progressionists were not rebels nor ashamed of the principles they had professed, and he

would be that one. The others, aghast at his resolve, tried
their utmost to dissuade him, but all to no purpose. Each in
turn then offered to stay in his place, but he would not hear
of it. It was more fitting, he replied, that he should remain,
because one of the oldest (he was just thirty years of age);
and forthwith, to signify that his resolve was unalterable,
he drew off his long court boots. Finding it impossible to
shake his determination, and fearing lest, if they delayed
longer, they might not escape themselves, they reluctantly
left him and fled. There in the palace, awaiting his certain
doom, the Chinese soldiers found him, a few minutes after.
They seized him and carried him to the Chinese camp,
where, with some show of formality, he was publicly executed. Thus died a brave and loyal soul, true with his life
to the principles he had publicly professed, and which he
deemed it cowardly and wicked to abandon. . . .

Meanwhile, the Japanese lay imprisoned within their legation buildings, closely besieged by the Koreans. Toward the
middle of the day, on the seventh, they discovered that their
provisions were nearly exhausted. Only the soldiers, therefore, were allowed rice, the rest getting for their portion the
water in which the rice had previously been boiled. There
were now in the compound one hundred and forty soldiers,
thirty servants attached to the legation, about seventy merchants and artisans, besides many other Japanese residents
from the city, who had sought refuge in the buildings. It was
utterly impossible to procure more provisions. Starvation
stared the prisoners in the face, even if they should contrive to
hold out against the assaults of the Koreans. Reports now
reached them that all the gates of Söul had been closed, and
that preparations were everywhere in progress for a general

attack. It was also rumored that this would take place at dusk, and that under cover of the darkness the legation would be fired by the foe.

Thereupon, Takezoye held a council of war, at which it was decided that the legation's only hope, desperate as it was deemed, lay in forcing a passage through the western gate of the city, and retreating as best they might to Chemulpo. Accordingly, at the close of the conference the order was given to withdraw from Söul. It was now discovered that the messenger to whom the letters were entrusted had been afraid to leave the legation. Doomed indeed seemed the ill-starred Korean attempt at a postal system to bring mishap upon everything connected with it, both big and little, new and old.

Takezoye then addressed the Japanese gathered in the court-yard. He told them that his guards had been obliged, in defense of the king on the preceding day, to fire upon the Chinese soldiers, who had broken into the palace and opened fire upon the royal apartments; that the Korean troops and people had now combined against the Japanese; that the Korean government was apparently powerless to protect them; that the legation was blockaded; that it was impossible longer to carry on the ministerial functions; and that he had resolved to retire upon Chemulpo, there to await instructions from Japan. All the confidential dispatches and other private documents belonging to the legation were then burned.

It was now half past two in the afternoon. The crowd without was steadily growing larger and larger, and closing in slowly but surely about the devoted compound. Suddenly, to its amazement, the outer wooden gates, so stoutly defended a few minutes before, swung inward; there was a moment's hush of expectation, and the Japanese column, grim with determination, defiled in marching order into the street. It was a sight to stir the most sluggish soul. Instinctively the Koreans fell back, awed as they read the desperate resolve in the faces of the men; and the column kept silently, surely, moving on. First came two detachments, forming the van; then the minister, his suite, the women and children, followed, placed in the centre and guarded on either hand by rows of soldiers. Next marched the secretaries and the subordinate officials of the legation, all armed, and with them the merchants and artisans, carrying the wounded and the ammunition. Two more detachments brought up the rear. Debouching into the main road, the body struck out for the western gate. The Koreans, who crowded the side-streets, the court-yards, and even the roofs of the houses, had by this time recovered from their first daze, and began to attack the column on all sides, firing and throwing stones. So poor was their aim, however, and so unused were they to the business, that neither bullets nor stones did the Japanese much harm. The vanguard, lying down in the road, fired at the assailants and drove them back, and the march proceeded. Nothing could stop the advance of the van, and the rear-guard as ably covered the rear. Slowly but surely the column pushed on.

It had thus got half-way across the city, when it encountered a more formidable obstruction. Opposite the old palace, where a broad avenue from the palace gates entered the road it was following, a detachment of the left division of the Korean army had been drawn up, to prevent, if possible, all escape. The spot was well chosen. On one side lay the army barracks of the left division, a safe retreat in case of failure, while in front stretched the broad, open space of the avenue, ending in the highway along which the Japanese were obliged to pass. To make the most of this position a field-piece had been brought out and trained on the cross-road, and deployed beside it the Koreans posted themselves, and waited for the coming column. As the foreigners came into view, marching across the end of the avenue, the Koreans opened fire upon them both with the field-piece and with small arms. The effect should have been frightful. As a matter of fact it was *nil*, owing to the same cause as before, the bullets passing some twenty feet over the heads of the Japanese. Not a single man was killed, and only a few were slightly wounded. The rear-guard, prone in the street or under cover of the little gutter-moats, a peculiar feature of all Korean city streets, calmly took accurate aim, and eventually forced this body of the enemy back into their barracks. Still harassed at every step by other troops and by the populace, the column, advancing steadily in spite of them, at last gained the west gate. It was shut, bolted, and guarded by Korean soldiers. A sudden onset of the vanguard put these to flight. Some of the soldiers, armed with axes, then severed the bars, demolished the heavy wooden doors, and the column passed through. Keeping up a fire on the foe, who still pursued, the Japanese then made for the principal ferry of the river Han, at a place called Marpo, one of the river suburbs of the city. As they turned there to look back toward Sŏul, they saw smoke rising from the direction of the legation, and knew from this that the buildings had already been fired. With the rear-guard set to protect the important points, they proceeded to cross the

stream. Seizing this opportunity, a parting attack was now
made by a conglomerate collection of Korean troops and
tramps, who had pursued them from the city. Hovering on
their flanks, these fired at the ferry boats as they passed over;
but the Japanese rear-guard shot at and killed some of them,
and so succeeded in keeping the others at bay. By about
half past five in the afternoon the Japanese had completed
the crossing. After this no further serious opposition was
made to their retreat, and, following the ordinary road and
marching the whole night, they reached the hill above
Chemulpo, and looked down upon the broad expanse of the
Yellow Sea at seven o'clock on the morning of the eighth.

The long, hard fight was over; an end had come at last.
They saw it in the sea stretched out at their feet, just awak-
ing from its lethargy at the touch of the morning light. To
them its gently heaving bosom spoke of their own return
to life. No crazy fishing boat now stood between them and
theirs. One of their own men-of-war lay at anchor in the
offing. There she rode, in all her stately beauty, the smoke
curling faintly upward from her funnel, waiting to bear
them across the water to the arms of those who held them
dear. And the sparkling shimmer, as the rays of the rising
sun tinged the Yellow Sea with gold in one long pathway
eastward, seemed Japan's own welcome sent to greet them,
a proud, fond smile from home.

CHAPTER VI

THE SOUL OF THE FAR EAST

BACK in Japan in the early spring of 1884, Percival stayed there until midsummer, when he turned his face homeward and westward, for he had crossed the Pacific three times and preferred to go home the other way. Touching at Shanghai and Hong Kong he stopped off at Singapore to make a detour to Java, which delayed him so much that he saw only the southern part of India. At Bombay he stayed with Charles Lowell, a cousin and class-mate, in charge of the branch there of the Comptoir d'Escompte of Paris; thence his route led through the Red Sea and Alexandria to Venice, where to his annoyance he was quarantined; not, as he sarcastically remarks, because he came from an infected country, but on account of cholera in the city itself. Finally he went home by way of Paris and London.

At this time he had clearly decided to write his book on Korea; for in his letters, and in memoranda in his letter book, are found many pages that appear afterwards therein. But he certainly had not lost his interest in mathematics or physics, for any casual observation would quickly bring it out. From the upper end of the Red Sea he sees a cloud casting a shadow on the desert toward Sinai, and proceeds to show how by the angle of elevation of the cloud, the angle of the sun, and the distance to the place where the shadow falls one can compute the height of the cloud. He looks at the reflection of the moon along the water and points out why, when there is a ripple on the surface, the track of light does not run directly toward the moon but to windward of it. All this was a matter of general intellectual alertness in a mind familiar with the subject, but there is as yet no indication that he had any intention of turning his attention to scientific pursuits. On the contrary, two letters written on this journey appear to show that he regarded literature, in a broad sense, as the field he proposed to enter, and with this his publications for several years to come accord.

In a letter from Bombay to Frederic J. Stimson,—a classmate who had already won his spurs by his pen, and was destined to go far,—he begins by speaking of his friend's writings, then of the subject in general, and finally turns to himself and says: "Somebody wrote me the other day apropos of what I may or may not write, that facts not reflections were the thing. Facts not reflections indeed. Why that is what most pleases mankind from the philosopher to the fair; one's own reflections on or from things. Are we to forego the splendor of the French salon which returns us beauty from a score of different points of view from its mirrors more brilliant than their golden settings. The fact gives us but a flat image. It is our reflections upon it that make it a solid truth. For every truth is many-sided. It has many aspects. We know now what was long unknown, that true seeing is done with the mind from the comparatively meagre material supplied by the eye. . . .

"I believe that all writing should be a collection of the

precious stones of truth which is beauty. Only the arrangement differs with the character of the book. You string them
into a necklace for the world at large. You pigeon-hole them
into drawers for the scientist. In the necklace you have the
calling of your thought; *i.e.,* the expressing of it and the
arrangement of the thoughts among themselves. I wonder
how many men are fortunate enough to have them come
as they are wanted. A question by the bye nearly incapable
of solution because what seems good to one man, does not
begin to satisfy the next."

A month later he writes to his mother from Paris on October 7th: "As for me, I wish I could believe a little more in
myself. It is at all times the one thing needful. As it is I
often get discouraged. You will—said Bigelow the other day
to me in Japan. There will be times when you will feel like
tearing the whole thing up and lighting your pipe with
the wreck. Don't you do it. Put it away and take it out
again at a less destructive moment." Then, speaking of
what his mother had written him, he says: "But I shall most
certainly act upon your excellent advice and what is more
you shall have the exquisite ennui of reading it before it
goes to print and then you know we can have corrections
and improvements by the family."

Reaching Boston in the autumn of 1884, he made it his
headquarters for the next four years. The period was far from
an idle one; for, apart from business matters that engaged
his attention, he was actively at work on two books: First,
the "Chosön," that study already described of Korea and
the account of his own sojourn there. The preface to this is
dated November 1885, and the publication was early in the
following year. The second book,—smaller in size and type,

and without illustrations,—is the most celebrated of his writings on the Orient. Its title, "The Soul of the Far East," denotes aptly its object in the mind of the author, for it is an attempt to portray what appeared to him the essential and characteristic difference between the civilizations of Eastern Asia and Western Europe. From an early time in his stay in Japan he had been impressed by what he called the impersonality of the people, the comparative absence, both in aspiration and in conduct, of diversified individual self-expression among them. The more he thought about it the stronger this impression became; and this book is a study of the subject in its various manifestations.

First comes a general discussion of the meaning and essence of individuality, with the deduction that the Japanese suffer from arrested development; that they have always copied but not assimilated; added but not incorporated the additions into their own civilization, like a tree into which have been grafted great branches while the trunk remains unchanged. "The traits that distinguished these peoples in the past have been gradually extinguishing them ever since. Of these traits, stagnating influences upon their career, perhaps the most important is the great quality of impersonality"; and later he adds, "Upon this quality as a foundation rests the Far Oriental character."

He then proceeds to demonstrate, or illustrate, his thesis from many aspects of Japanese life, beginning with the family. He points out that no one has a personal birthday or even age of his own, two days in the year being treated as universal birthdays, one for girls and the other for boys, the latter, in May, being the occasion when hollow paper fish are flown from poles over every house where a boy

has been born during the preceding year. Everyone, moreover, is credited with a year's advance in age on New Year's
Day quite regardless of the actual date of his birth. If a
youth "belongs to the middle class, as soon as his schooling"
in the elements of the Classics "is over he is set to learn his
father's trade. To undertake to learn any trade but his
father's would strike the family as simply preposterous."
But to whatever class he may belong he is taught the duty
of absolute subordination to the head of the family, for the
family is the basis of social life in the Far East. Marriage,
with us a peculiarly personal matter, is in the East a thing
in which the young people have no say whatever; it is
a business transaction conducted by the father through
marriage brokers. A daughter becoming on marriage a
part of her husband's family ceases to be a member of her
own, and her descendants are no benefit to it, unless, per-
chance, having no brothers, one of her sons is adopted by
her father. Thus it is that when a child is born the general joy "depends somewhat upon the sex. If the baby
chances to be a boy, everybody is immensely pleased; if
a girl there is considerably less effusion shown. In the
latter case the more impulsive relatives are unmistakably
sorry; the more philosophic evidently hope for better luck
next time. Both kinds make very pretty speeches, which
not even the speakers believe, for in the babe lottery the
family is considered to have drawn a blank. A delight so
engendered proves how little of the personal, even in pro-
spective, attaches to its object."

In the fourth chapter he takes up the question of language,
bringing out his point with special effect, showing the absence of personal pronouns, and indeed of everything that

indicates an expression of individuality or even of sex, re-
placing them by honorifics which occur in the most surprising way. But the matter of language, though highly
significant, is somewhat technical, and his discussion can
be left to those who care to follow it in his book.

He turns next to nature and to art, pointing out how genuine, how universal, and at the same time how little individual, how impersonal, is the Japanese love of those things.
Of them he says "that nature, not man, is their *beau idéal,*
the source to them of inspiration, is evident again in looking at their art." Incidentally, the account of the succession of flower festivals throughout the year is a beautiful
piece of descriptive writing, glowing with the color it portrays and the delight of the throngs of visitors.

On the subject of religion he has much to say. Shintoism,
though generally held by the people, and causing great numbers of them to go as pilgrims to the sacred places on mountain tops, he regards as not really a religion. That is the reason
it is not inconsistent with Buddhism. "It is not simply that
the two contrive to live peaceably together; they are actually
both of them implicitly believed by the same individual.
Millions of Japanese are good Buddhists and good Shin-
toists at the same time. That such a combination should be
possible is due to the essential difference in the character of
the two beliefs. The one is extrinsic, the other intrinsic, in
its relations to the human soul. Shintoism tells a man but
little about himself and his hereafter; Buddhism, little but
about himself and what he may become. In examining
Far Eastern religion, therefore, for personality, or the reverse, we may dismiss Shintoism as having no particular
bearing upon the subject." Turning to the other system he

says: "At first sight Buddhism is much more like Christianity than those of us who stay at home and speculate upon it commonly appreciate. As a system of philosophy it sounds exceedingly foreign, but it looks unexpectedly familiar as a faith." After dwelling upon the resemblances in the popular attitude, he continues: "But behind all this is the religion of the few,—of those to whom sensuous forms cannot suffice to represent super-sensuous cravings; whose god is something more than an anthropomorphic creation; to whom worship means not the cramping of the body, but the expansion of the soul." . . . "In relation to one's neighbor the two beliefs are kin, but as regards one's self, as far apart as the West is from the East. For here, at this idea of self, we are suddenly aware of standing on the brink of a fathomless abyss, gazing giddily down into that great gulf which divides Buddhism from Christianity. We cannot see the bottom. It is a separation more profound than death; it seems to necessitate annihilation. To cross it we must bury in its depths all we know as ourselves.

"Christianity is a personal religion; Buddhism, an impersonal one. In this fundamental difference lies the worldwide opposition of the two beliefs. Christianity tells us to purify ourselves that we may enjoy countless aeons of that bettered self hereafter; Buddhism would have us purify ourselves that we may lose all sense of self for evermore."

At the end of this chapter he sums up his demonstration thus: "We have seen, then, how in trying to understand these peoples we are brought face to face with impersonality in each of those three expressions of the human soul, speech, thought, yearning. We have looked at them first from a social standpoint. We have seen how singularly little regard is paid the individual from his birth to his death. How he lives his life long the slave of patriarchal customs of so puerile a tendency as to be practically impossible to a people really grown up. How he practises a wholesale system of adoption sufficient of itself to destroy any surviving regard for the ego his other relations might have left. How in his daily life he gives the minimum of thought to the bettering himself in any worldly sense, and the maximum of polite consideration to his neighbor. How, in short, he acts toward himself as much as possible as if he were another, and to that other as if he were himself.

"Then, not content with standing stranger-like upon the threshold, we have sought to see the soul of their civilization in its intrinsic manifestations. We have pushed our inquiry, as it were, one step nearer its home. And the same trait that was apparent sociologically has been exposed in this our antipodal phase of psychical research. We have seen how impersonal is his language, the principal medium of communication between one soul and another; how impersonal are the communings of his soul with itself. How the man turns to nature instead of to his fellowman in silent sympathy. And how, when he speculates upon his coming castles in the air, his most roseate desire is to be but an indistinguishable particle of the sunset clouds and vanish invisible as they into the starry stillness of all-embracing space.

"Now what does this strange impersonality betoken? Why are these peoples so different from us in this most fundamental of considerations to any people, the consideration of themselves? The answer leads to some interesting conclusions."

The final chapter is entitled "Imagination," for he regards

this as the source of all progress, and the far orientals as particularly unimaginative. Their art he ascribes to appreciation rather than originality. They are, he declares, less advanced than the occidentals, their rate of progress is less rapid and the individuals are more alike; and he concludes that unless their newly imported ideas really take root they will vanish "off the face of the earth and leave our planet the eventual possession of the dwellers where the day declines."

One cannot deny that he made a strong case for the impersonality of the Japanese; and if it be thought that his conclusions therefrom were unfriendly it must be remembered that he had a deep admiration and affection for that people, wishing them well with all his heart.

Without attempting to survey the reviews and criticisms of the book, which was translated into many languages, it may be interesting to recall the comments of three Europeans of very diverse qualities and experiences. Dr. Pierre Janet, the great French neurologist, said to a friend of the author that as a study of Japanese mentality it seemed to him to show more insight than any other he had ever read on the subject.

The second commentator is Lafcadio Hearn, a very different type of person, given to enthusiasm. He had not yet been to Japan, and "The Soul of the Far East" had much to do with his going there. In his book "Concerning Lafcadio Hearn" George M. Gould says:

"Perhaps I should not have succeeded in getting Hearn to attempt Japan had it not been for a little book that fell into his hands during the stay with me. Beyond question, Mr. Lowell's volume had a profound influence in turning his attention to Japan and greatly aided me in my insistent urging him to go there. In sending the book Hearn wrote me this letter:

"Gooley!—I have found a marvellous book,—a book of books! —a colossal, splendid, godlike book. You must read every line of it. For heaven's sake don't skip a word of it. The book is called "The Soul of the Far East," but its title is smaller than its imprint.

HEARNEYBOY

"P.S. Let something else go to H—, and read this book instead. May God eternally bless and infinitely personalize the man who wrote this book! Please don't skip one solitary line of it, and don't delay reading it,—because something, much! is going to go out of this book into your heart and life and stay there! I have just finished this book and feel like John in Patmos,—only a d——d sight better. He who shall skip one word of this book let his portion be cut off and his name blotted out of the Book of Life."

Hearn had read the book on Korea and was impressed by that also, for in a letter of 1889, he wrote, after commenting on another work he had been reading, "How luminous and psychically electric is Lowell's book compared with it. And how much nobler a soul must be the dreamer of Chosön!" [1]

After living in Japan Hearn came to different conclusions about Percival's ideas on the impersonality of the Japanese, but he never lost his admiration for the book or its author. In May, 1891, he writes;

"Mr. Lowell has, I think, no warmer admirer in the world than myself, though I do not agree with his theory in "The Soul of the Far East," and think he has ignored the most essential and astonishing quality of the race: its genius of eclecticism." [2]

[1] "The Life and Letters of Lafcadio Hearn by Elizabeth Bisland," Vol. I, p. 459.
[2] Ib., Vol. II, p. 28.

And again,

"I am not vain enough to think I can ever write anything so beautiful as his "Chosön" or "Soul of the Far East," and will certainly make a poor showing beside his precise, fine, perfectly worded work." [3]

And, finally, as late as 1902 he speaks of it as "incomparably the greatest of all books on Japan, and the deepest." [4]

The third European critic to be quoted is Dr. Clay Macauley, a Unitarian missionary to Japan, who had been a friend of Percival's there, and after his death at Flagstaff in 1916 was still at work among the Japanese. On January 24, 1917, he read before the Asiatic Society of Japan a Memorial to him, in which he gave an estimate of "The Soul of the Far East":

"The year after the publication of "Cho-son," the book which has associated Lowell most closely with a critical and interpretative study of the peoples and institutions of this part of the world, appeared his much-famed "Soul of the Far East." I have no time for an extended critique of this marvellous ethnic essay. "Marvellous" I name it, not only because of the startling message it bears and the exquisitely fascinating speech by which the message is borne, but also because of the revelation it gives of the distinctive mental measure and the characteristic personality of the author himself . . . the book is really a marvellous psychical study. However, in reading it today, the critical reader should, all along, keep in mind the time and conditions under which Lowell wrote. His judgment of "The Soul of the Far East" was made

[3] *Ib.*, Vol. II, p. 30.
[4] *Ib.*, Vol. II, p. 487. See also pp. 479, 505. Percival's "Occult Japan" a study of Shinto trances, published in 1894, he did not like at all. It struck him only "as a mood of the man, an ugly supercilious one, verging on the wickedness of a wish to hurt—there was in 'The Soul of the Far East' an exquisite approach to playful tenderness—utterly banished from 'Occult Japan.' " *Id.*, pp. 204, 208. By this time Hearn seems to have come to resent criticism of the Japanese.

fully a generation ago. Time has brought much change to all
Oriental countries since then, especially to this "Land of the Rising Sun."

He then refers to the author's conviction that owing to
their impersonality the Oriental people, if unchanged and
unless their newly imported ideas take root, would disappear
before the advancing nations of the West, and proceeds:

"Now, notice Lowell's "ifs" and "unless." He had passed his
judgment; but he saw a possible transformation. And I know
that he hailed the incoming into the East of the motive forces of
the West as forerunner of a possible ascendancy here of the
genius of the world's advancing civilization, prophetic of that
New East into which, now, the Far East is becoming wonder-
ously changed."

Japan certainly is not in a process of disappearing before
the advancing nations of the West; but it may be that this
is not because her people have radically changed their
nature. The arts of the West, civil and military, they have
thoroughly acquired; but Percival Lowell may have been
right in his diagnosis and wrong in his forecast. His estimate of their temperament may have been correct, and the
conclusion therefrom of their destiny erroneous. The
strange identity with which all Japanese explain the recent
international events is not inconsistent with his theory of
impersonality, and it may be that from a national standpoint this is less a source of weakness than of strength.

CHAPTER VII

SECOND VISIT TO JAPAN

HAVING got "The Soul of the Far East" off his hands, and into those of the public, in 1888, he sailed in December for Japan, arriving on January the eighth. As usual he took a house in Tokyo and on January 23 he writes to his mother about it. "My garden is a miniature range of hills on one side, a dry pond on the other. One plum tree is blooming now, another comes along shortly, and a cherry tree will peep into my bedroom window all a-blush toward the beginning of April. A palm tree exists with every appearance of comfort in front of the drawing room, a foreground for the hills.

"The fictitious employment by the Japanese has developed into a real one most amusingly—You know by the existing law a foreigner is not allowed to live outside of the foreign reservation unless in the service of some native body, governmental or private. Now Chamberlain got a Mr. Masujima to arrange matters. The plan that occurred to him, Masujima, was to employ me to lecture before the School of Languages of which he, Masujima, is President. It was thought better to make the thing in part real, a suggestion I liked, and the upshot of it is that I am booked to deliver a lecture a week until I see fit to change. Chamberlin and Masujima cooked up between them the idea of translating

41

my initial performance and then inserting it in a reader
of lectures, sermons and such in the colloquiae which Chamberlain is preparing—Subject—A homily to the students to
become superior Japanese rather than inferior Europeans.
Curious if you will in view of the fact that Masujima himself is madly in love with foreigners and as C. says is a sort
of universal solvent for their quandaries."

January 1889 proved a peculiarly fortunate time to arrive,
for most interesting events were about to take place, as he
soon wrote to his old college chum, Harcourt Amory, on
February 21:

"Things have been happening since I arrived. Indeed I
could hardly have lit upon a more eventful month—from
doings of the Son of Heaven to those of Mother Earth—
the transmigration from the old to the new palace, the ceremony of the promulgation of the Constitution, and the
earthquake, and the assassination of Mori—and his burial
the most huge affair of years. How he was murdered on
the morning of the great national event just as he was setting out for the palace by a fanatic in the ante-chamber of
his own house because two years ago he trod on the mats
at Ise with his boots and poked the curtains aside with his
cane—you have probably already heard—For the affair was
too dramatic to have escaped European and American newspapers. The to us significant part of the story is the quasi
sublatent approval of large numbers of Japanese. The whole
procedure of the assassin commends itself in method to their
ideas of the way to do it. The long cherished plan, the visit
to the temples of Ise for corroboration of facts, the selec-
tion of the day, the coolness shown beforehand, the facing
of death in return, the very blows à la hari-kiri etc., all tout-

a-fait comme il faut. How he went to a joroya (house of prostitution) the night before, saying that he wished to have experienced as many phases of life as possible before leaving it, how the official who received him at Mori's house (he introduced himself by the story that he had come to warn Mori of a plot to assassinate him) could recall no signs of nervousness in him, except that he lifted his teacup to drink once or twice after he had emptied it.

"The whole affair appeals to their imaginations, showing still a pretty state of society. They also admire the beautiful way the guard killed him, decapitating him in the good old-fashioned way just leaving his head hanging to his neck by a strip—Pleasing details."

The story of the murder of Mori, and of the public festivities that were going on at the time, he told under the title of "The Fate of a Japanese Reformer" in the *Atlantic Monthly* for November 1890. It is perhaps the best of his descriptive writings, for the tragedy and its accessories are full of striking contrasts which he brought out with great effect. After a prelude on the danger of attempting changes too rapidly, he gives a brief account of the life of Mori Arinori; how in his youth he was selected to study abroad, how he did so in America, and became enamored of occidental ways, returning in time for the revolution that restored the Mikado. He threw himself into the new movement, rose in office, and, as he did so, strove to carry out his ideas. He was the first to propose disarming the *samurai,* which against bitter opposition was accomplished. As Minister of Education he excluded religion from all national instruction. He even suggested that the native language should be superseded by a modified English, the

American people to adopt the changes also; but the plan obtained no support on either side of the Pacific.

The Japanese reformers felt that like almost all Western nations Japan should have a written constitution, and they set the date for its promulgation at February 11th, 1889. This Percival thought a mistake since it was the festival of Jimmu Tenno, the mythic founder of the imperial house. Nevertheless, the reformers, who had virtual control of the government, determined that the two celebrations should take place on the same day; and he describes the gorgeous decoration of the city as he saw it, the functions attending the grant of the constitution, and processions of comic chariots in honor of Jimmu Tenno. To a foreigner the strange mixture of native and partially imitated European costumes was irresistibly funny; but the populace enjoyed themselves. "The rough element," he says, "so inevitable elsewhere was conspicuously absent. There is this great gain among a relatively less differentiated people. If you miss with regret the higher brains, you miss with pleasure the lower brutes. *Bons enfants* the Japanese are to a man. They gather delight as men have learned to extract sugar, from almost anything. . . . As the twilight settled over the city, a horrible rumor began to creep through the streets. During the day the thing would seem to have shrunk before the mirth of the masses, but under the cover of gloom it spread like night itself over the town. It passed from mouth to mouth with something of the shudder with which a ghost might come and go. Viscount Mori, Minister of State for Education, had been murdered that morning in his own house. . . .

"What had happened was this:—

"While Viscount Mori was dressing, on the morning of

the 11th, for the court ceremony of the promulgation of the new Constitution, a man, unknown to the servants, made summons on the big bell hung by custom at the house entrance, and asked to see the Minister on important business. He was told the Minister was dressing, and could see no one. The unknown replied that he must see him about a matter of life and death,—as indeed it was. The apparent gravity of the object induced the servant to admit him to an antechamber and report the matter. In consequence, the Minister's private secretary came down to interview him. The man, who seemed well behaved, informed the secretary that there was a plot to take the Minister's life, and that he had come to warn the Minister of it. Truly a subtle subterfuge; true to the letter, since the plot was all his own. More he refused to divulge except to the Minister himself. While the secretary was trying to learn something more definite, Mori came down stairs, and entered the room. The unknown approached to speak to him; then, suddenly drawing a knife from his girdle, sprang at him, and crying 'This for desecrating the shrines of Ise!' stabbed him twice in the stomach. Mori, taken by surprise, grappled with him, when one of his body guards, hearing the noise, rushed in, and with one blow of his sword almost completely severed the man's head from his body.

"Meanwhile, Mori had fallen to the floor, bleeding fast. The secretary, with the help of the guard, raised him, carried him to his room, and despatched a messenger for the court surgeon.

"The clothes of the unknown were then searched for some clue to the mystery; for neither Mori nor any of his household had ever seen him before. The search proved more than successful. A paper was found on his person, setting forth in a most circumstantial manner the whole history of his crime, from its inception to its execution, or his own. However reticent he seemed before the deed, he evidently meant nothing should be hid after it, whether he succeeded or not. The paper explained the reason.

"Because, it read, of the act of sacrilege committed by Mori Arinori, who, on a visit to the shrines of Ise, two years before, had desecrated the temple by pushing its curtain back with his cane, and had defiled its floor by treading upon it with his boots, he, Nishino Buntaro, had resolved to kill Mori, and avenge the insult offered to the gods and to the Emperor, whose ancestors they were. To wipe the stain from the national faith and honor, he was ready to lose his life, if necessary. He left this paper as a memorial of his intent."

In the meantime the messenger sent for the court surgeon failed to find him, for he was at the palace. The same was true of the next in rank, and when at last a surgeon was found Mori had lost so much blood that in the night of the following day he died.

Both by his opinions and his tactless conduct as a minister Mori had made himself unpopular and rumors that his life was in danger had been current for two or three days. "If Mori was thus a very definite sort of person, Nishino was quite as definite in his own way." At the time of his crime he held a post in the Home Department, where he brooded over the insult to the gods. "He seems to have heard of it accidentally, but it made so much impression upon him that he journeyed to Ise to find out the truth of the tale. He was convinced, and forthwith laid his plans with the single-

ness of zeal of a fanatic," as appears from his affectionate
farewell letters to his father and his younger brother.

"But the strangest and most significant part of the affair
was the attitude of the Japanese public toward it. The first
excitement of the news had not passed before it became evident that their sympathy was not with the murdered man,
but with his murderer. . . . Nishino was an unknown. . . .
Yet the sentiment was unmistakable. The details of the
murder were scarcely common property before the press
proceeded to eulogize the assassin. To praise the act was a
little too barefaced, not to say legally dangerous. . . . But
to praise the man became a journalistic epidemic. . . .
Nishino, they said, had contrived and executed his plan
with all the old time *samurai* bravery. He had done it as a
samurai should have done it, and he had died as a *samurai*
should have died. . . . The summary action of the guard in
cutting the murderer down was severely censured. As if the
guard had not been appointed to this very end! . . . The
papers demanded the guard's arrest and trial. . . . Com-
ment of this kind was not confined to the press. Strange as
it may appear, the newspapers said what everybody thought.
. . . There was no doubt about it. Beneath the surface of
decorous disapproval ran an undercurrent of admiration and
sympathy, in spots but ill hid. People talked in the same
strain as the journalists wrote. Some did more than talk.
The geisha, or professional singing girls of Tokyo, made of
Nishino and his heroism a veritable cult. . . . His grave
in the suburbs they kept wreathed with flowers. To it they
made periodic pilgrimages, and, bowing there to the gods,
prayed that a little of the hero's spirit might descend on
them. The practice was not a specialty of professionals.

Persons of all ages and both sexes visited the spot in shoals, for similar purposes. It became a mecca for a month. The thing sounds incredible, but it was a fact. Such honor had been paid nobody for years."

This in abstract is Percival's account of a terrible national tragedy, and its amazing treatment by the public at large.

Before he had been long in Japan the old love of travel into regions unknown to foreigners came back. He had already visited some of the less frequented parts of the interior, and now scanning, one evening, the map of the country his eye was caught by the pose of a province that stood out in graphic mystery, as he said, from the western coast. It made a striking figure with its deep-bosomed bays and its bold headlands. Its name was Noto; and the more he looked the more he longed, until the desire simply carried him off his feet. Nobody seemed to know much about it, for scarcely a foreigner had been there; and, in fact, he set his heart on going to Noto just because it was not known. That is his own account of the motive for the journey he made early in May, 1889; which turned out somewhat of a disappointment, for the place was not, either in its physical features or the customs of its people, very different from the rest of Japan; but for him proved adventurous and highly interesting. Under the title of "Noto" he gave an account of it,—as usual after his return home in the following spring,—first by a series of articles in the *Atlantic,* and then as a book published in 1891. It is a well-told tale of a journey, quite exciting, where he and his porters, in seeking to scale a mountain pass, found their way lay along precipices where the path had crumbled into the gorge below. The descriptions of people and scenery are vigorous and terse; but the book is not a philosophic study like those on Korea and on Japanese psychology. Yet it is notable in showing his versatility, as is also the fact that he gave the ΦBK poem at Harvard in June of that year.

Hurrying home to deliver that poem, shortly after his return from Noto, he found himself busy for a year and a half, writing, attending to his own affairs, and to business, for he was part of the time, as Treasurer, the manager of the Lowell Bleachery. Meanwhile his hours of leisure were filled with a new and absorbing avocation, that of polo.

As a boy at Brookline, Patrick Burns, the coachman, trained at Newcastle, had taught him to ride bareback with a halter for a bridle—although he had never really cared for riding, just as in college he had run races without taking much interest in athletics. But on August 9, 1887, we find him writing that he has bought a polo pony, and that "Sam Warren, Fred Stimson, et al. have just started a polo club at Dedham, and have also in contemplation the erection of an inn there." He adds that he is in both schemes; and in fact the plan for an inn developed into a clubhouse, where he lived in summer for some years when about Boston. During the remainder of the first season the players knocked the ball about—and rarely with a full team of four in a side —tried to learn the game on a little field belonging to George Nickerson, another member of the club. But the next year the number increased, and Percival with his great quickness and furious energy soon forged ahead, leading the list of home handicaps in the club with a rating of ten, and becoming the first captain of the team.

By the autumn of 1888 they had become expert enough to play a match with the Myopia club on its grounds at Ham-

ilton, but with unfortunate results. At that time it was the
habit to open the game by having the ball thrown into the
middle of the field, and at a signal the leading player from
each side charged from his goal posts, each trying to reach
the ball first. Percival had a very fast pony, so had George
von L. Meyer on the other side, and by some misunderstand-
ing about the rules of turning there was a collision. In an
instant both men and both horses were flat on the field.
Percival was the most hurt, and although he mounted his
horse and tried to play, he was too much stunned to be
effective, and had to withdraw from the game.

In the following years he played as captain other match
games with various teams; and, in fact, the Dedham Polo
Club, which he came to regard as his home, was certainly
his chief resource for recreation and diversion in this country until he built his Observatory in Arizona. Yet it by no
means absorbed his attention, for with all the vigor he threw
into anything he undertook he could maintain an intense
interest in several things at the same time, besides being always ready for new ones, not least in the form of travel. So
it happened that at the end of January, 1890, he sailed again
for Europe, and with Ralph Curtis, a friend from boyhood
and a college classmate, visited Spain—not in this case to
study the people or the land, although he observed what he
saw with care, but for the pleasure and experience. Like all
good travellers he went to Seville for Holy Week and the
festivities following; but, being sensitive, the bullfight was a
thing to be seen rather than enjoyed. He had heard people
speak also of the cathedral of Burgos as marvellous, in fact
as the finest specimen in the world; so, at some inconven-
ience, he went there on his way to France, and on seeing it

remarked that the praise bestowed upon it was due less to its merits than to its inaccessibility. Later he noticed that having taken the trouble to go to Burgos he never heard anyone speak of it again. So much for people's estimates of things someone else has not seen.

On his way home he passed through London and enjoyed the hospitality he always found there.

CHAPTER VIII

JAPAN AGAIN—THE SHINTO TRANCES

THE trip to Spain was merely an interlude; for, above all, at this time he felt the attraction of Japan. Returning from Europe in June he spent the summer in Dedham; but when winter came he started again for the Far East, this time by way of Europe, where he picked up Ralph Curtis; and then by the Red Sea to India and Burma, reaching Tokyo about the first of April, 1891. By far the most interesting part of this visit to Japan arose from a journey which he took with George Agassiz in July and August, into the interior of the Island. Agassiz became a most devoted friend, who followed his studies here, and later in Flagstaff, taking part in his observations and writing a memorial after his death. Their object was travel through a part of the mountainous region, ending at Ontake, a high extinct volcano, one of Japan's most sacred peaks. But the holiness of the spot, or the religious pilgrimages thereto, were not the motive of the visit; nor did they expect to see anything of that nature with which they were not already familiar.

Leaving Tokyo by train on July 24, they soon reached a point where they got off and took jinrikishas to descend later to their own feet on a path that came "out every now and then over a view at spots where Agassiz said one had to be careful not to step over into the view one's self." For the

next three days the lodging was not too comfortable, the
heat terrific and the footpath going over a steep mountain
pass. However, the weather improved; and without serious
misadventure they were, on August 6, ascending Ontake,
and not far from the top, when they saw three young men,
clad as pilgrims, begin a devotional ceremony. One of them
seated on a bench before a shrine, went through what looked
like contortions accompanied by a chant, while another, at
whom they were directed, sat bowed on the opposite bench
motionless until, beginning to twitch, he broke into a
paroxysm and ended by becoming stiff though still quiver-
ing. Then the first leaned forward, and bowing down, asked
the name of the god that possessed his companion. The
other in a strange voice answered "I am Hakkai." Whereat
the first asked, as of an oracle, questions that were answered;
and after the god had finished speaking, said a prayer and
woke the other from his trance. But this was not the end, for
the same thing was repeated, the three changing places by
rotation until each of them had been petitioner and en-
tranced. On several more occasions the ceremony was en-
acted during the next thirty-six hours, the young men fasting
all that time. The whole scene is more fully described in the
opening chapter of Percival's "Occult Japan."

With his temperament and literary ambition he thought
at once of writing about this extraordinary sight, which he
connected as a phenomenon with the fox possession he had
already encountered on a lower plane. He suggested the
title "Ontake, a Pilgrimage," but he soon saw the whole
matter on a larger scale. The cult seemed to be unknown
beyond its votaries, nothing did he find written upon it,
the few foreigners who had scaled the mountain had missed

it altogether, although, as he says, their guides or porters must have been familiar with it. Dr. Sturgis Bigelow, who was a student and believer in Buddhism, had never heard of it, which seemed strange, for although a Shinto, not a Buddhist, rite many people accepted both faiths, and one Buddhist sect practiced something akin to it. Moreover, its underlying idea of possession by another spirit appeared to ramify, not only into fox possession, but in many other directions. On inquiry he found that there was an establishment of the Ontake cult in Tokyo, and the head of it the Kwanchō, or primate of that Shinto sect. This man proved very friendly and gave all the information about its rites, their significance and underlying philosophy, within his knowledge,—perhaps beyond it,—and arranged exhibits; all of which Percival carefully recorded in his notebooks. Every motion made in inducing the trance, every implement used in the ceremony, had its meaning and its function, which he strove to learn. Moreover, there were miracles of splashing with boiling water, walking over hot coals and up ladders with sword blades for rungs; curing disease; consulting the fox and the raccoon-faced dog, which he called Japanese table turning; and other less dignified performances more or less connected with the idea of divine or demonic possession. Some of these things he was able to witness by séances in his own house, others by visits to the places where they were performed, often for his special benefit.

All this took more time than he had expected to spend in Japan, and delayed his sailing until the autumn was more than half over. Nor was this enough to complete his researches. In December of the following year he re-crossed the Pacific, and at Christmas we find him at Yokohama.

Again he hires a house, fits it up in Japanese style but with occidental furniture; again he was travelling over the land, this time in search less of scenery than of psychic phenomena and the lore connected with their celebration. In July he is interviewing a Ryobu Shinto priest and "eliciting much valuable information."

For the trances, and the various miracles, a participant must be prepared by a process of purification, long continued for the former, always by bathing before the ceremony; and by Percival's frequent attendance, and great interest, he attained the repute for a degree of purity that enabled him to go where others were not admitted. On this ground he attended what he called the Kwanchō's Kindergarten, but was not allowed to bring a friend. The Kwanchō, as the head of the principal Shinto sect that practised trances, had a class of boys and girls who went through a preparation therefor by a series of what an unbeliever might call ecstatic acrobatic feats, lasting a long time before they were fitted for subjects of divine possession. He visited everything relating to the mysteries that he could find, procured from the Kwanchō an introduction that enabled him to see the interior grounds of the great shrines of Ise, from which even the pilgrims were excluded, and to see there a building whereof he learned the history and meaning that the very guardian priests did not understand. At trances he was allowed to examine the possessed, take their pulse, and even to stick pins into them to test their sensibility, sometimes in a way that they were far from not feeling afterwards. In short he was enabled as no one had ever been before, to make a very thorough examination of the phenomena with the object of discovering and revealing their significance; for he was convinced that they were perfectly genuine, without a tinge of fraud, and allied to the hypnotism then at the height of its vogue. In March, 1893 he gave the first of a series of papers on Esoteric Shintoism before the Asiatic Society of Japan. These he worked up after his return to America in the autumn, and published in 1895 with the title "Occult Japan or the Way of the Gods."

A casual reader might be misled by occasional cleverness of expression into thinking the book less serious than it is. Perhaps that accounts in part for Lafcadio Hearn's calling it supercilious. Percival himself says, in the first paragraph of the chapter on Miracles: "It is quite possible to see the comic side of things without losing sight of their serious aspect. In fact, not to see both sides is to get but a superficial view of life, missing its substance. So much for the people. As for the priests, it is only necessary to say that few are more essentially sincere and lovable than the Shintō ones; and few religions in a sense more true. With this preface for life-preserver I plunge boldly into the miracles." In fact, expressions that appear less serious than the subject merits are few, and the descriptions, of the trances for example, are almost strangely appreciative, and for a scientific study keenly sympathetic and beautiful.

The book opens with an account of the trances of the three young men on Mount Ontake, for that sight was the source of all these researches. He next lays a foundation for the study of the subject by a short history of the Japanese religions; how Shinto, the old cult, with its myriad divinities and simple rites, was for a time overshadowed by Buddhism, to be restored with the power of the Mikado; and how with its revival the popularity of the trances returned. They had been kept alive by a single Buddhist sect which had adopted them, but now they are even more widely practised by two out of the ten Shinto sects, their sacred site being Ontake. But before taking up the trances he describes the lesser, and better known, cases of miraculous intervention for protection from injury and for sanctification; notably, being sprinkled with boiling water, walking over a bed of hot coals, and up and down a ladder of sword blades; and he discusses why no injury occurs. The walking over hot coals, at least, was even performed in his own garden; and, although he does not say so in the book, he did it himself, without, however, complete immunity to the soles of his feet.

After telling of what he terms objective, as distinguished from subjective, miracles, such as bringing down fire from heaven; and saying something of miraculous healing of disease, he comes to the main subject of the book, the incarnations or trances. First he speaks of the preparation for them, washing and fasting which are arduous and long, the purification of persons and places, and a series of ceremonies which, he says, tend to promote vacuity of mind. All these things are absolutely sincere, for he declares that the first view of a trance dispels any idea of sham. He then describes three typical trances: first Ryobu, a Shinto-Buddhist sect, where one of the men possessed, on coming back to himself, was disappointed that he had not spoken English, which he did not know himself; for to his mind it was not he that spoke but the god who entered into him. The second example was a Buddhist trance with the full complement of eight persons filling their several offices in the ceremony. This description is especially striking and sympathetic. The

third case is of a pure Shinto trance, much the same, but with
the simpler ceremonial of that cult. He describes also the
Kwanchō's training school, which has already been referred
to as the Kindergarten. He notes the pulse, insensibility, the
other physical conditions and sensations of the possessed, the
sex and number of the gods who enter him, for the exorcist
has no power to invoke the spirit he would prefer, but simply calls for a god, and when one comes inquires who it is. It
may be a god or a goddess, and several of them may come in
succession. The main object of the proceeding being to obtain counsel or prophecy, the exorcist, and he alone, can ask
questions of him, but he can do so on behalf of anyone
else, and often did so for Percival about his own affairs, although the prophecies appear never to have turned out
right.

A chapter is devoted to pilgrimages and the pilgrim clubs,
which included in the aggregate vast numbers of people,
only a minute part of whom, however, belonged to the
trance sects. They subscribed small sums to be used to send
each year a few of their members to the shrine or sacred
mountain with which the club is associated; this feature of
the religious organization being as important from a social
as a religious point of view. Another chapter is given to the
Gohei, or sacred cluster of paper strips, used for all spiritual
purposes, and essential in calling down any god; an emblem
which he compares with the crucifix, while pointing out the
difference in their use. This first part of the book ends with
an argument, apparently to one who knows nothing about
the matter conclusive, that the whole subject of these trances
is of Shinto not Buddhist origin; and in this connection he
tells of his visit to the shrines of Ise where a temple was built

to the sun-goddess when she possessed people, as she has long ceased to do at these shrines.

So far the book is scientific; that is, it consists of a description and analysis of phenomena repeatedly observed and carefully tested. The second part, which he calls Noumena, is an explanation of them on general psychological principles, and thus belongs rather to philosophy than science. It comprises discussions of the essence of self, of the freedom of the will, of the motive forces of ideas, of individuality, of dreams, hypnotism and trances. In these matters he was much influenced by the recently published "Psychology" of William James, which he had with him, and he draws comparisons with hypnotism, a more prominent subject then than it is now. Bearing in mind his dominant thought about the essential quality of the Japanese, it is not unnatural that he should find in the greater frequency of such phenomena among them than elsewhere a confirmation of his theory of their comparative lack of personality.

Perhaps his own estimate of the relative value of the two parts of the book and that of critics might not agree; but, however that may be, the second part is penetrating, and the work as a whole a remarkable study of a subject up to that time practically wholly concealed from the many observers of Japanese life and customs. It was, in fact, his farewell to Japan, for, leaving in the fall of 1893, he never again visited that land. Ten years its people had been his chief intellectual interest, but perhaps he thought he had exhausted the vein in which he had been at work, or another interest may have dislodged it. He has left no statement of why he gave up Japan for astronomy, but probably there is truth in both of these conjectures.

Talking later to George Agassiz, Percival attributed the change to the fact that Schiaparelli, who had first observed the fine lines on the planet Mars which he called "canali," found that his failing eyesight prevented his pursuing his observations farther, and that he had determined to carry them on. That may well have directed his attention to the particular planet; but the interest in astronomy lay far deeper, extending back to the little telescope of boyhood on the roof of his father's house at Brookline. We have seen that his Commencement Part at graduation was on the nebular hypothesis, and he never lost his early love of such things. In July, 1891, he writes to his brother-in-law, William L. Putnam, about a project for writing on what he calls the philosophy of the cosmos, with illustrations from celestial mechanics. That was just before he went to Ontake and there became involved in the study of trances, "which," as he says in his next letter to the same, "adds another to my budget of literary eventualities." In fact, the trances occupied most of his time for the next two years, without banishing the thought of later taking up other things, or effacing the lure of astronomy, for in 1892 he took with him to Japan a six-inch telescope, no small encumbrance unless really desired, and he writes of observing Saturn therewith. Whatever may have been the reason, it seems probable from the rapidity with which he threw himself into astronomy and into its planetary branch, that at least he had something of the kind in his mind before he returned from Japan in the autumn of 1893.

CHAPTER IX

THE OBSERVATORY AT FLAGSTAFF

W<small>HEN</small>, returning from Japan late in 1893, Percival Lowell found himself quickly absorbed by astronomical research, he was by no means without immediate equipment for the task. His mathematical capacity, that in college had so impressed Professor Benjamin Peirce, had not been allowed to rust away; for, when at home, he had kept it bright in the Mathematical and Physical (commonly called the M. P.) Club, a group of men interested in the subject, mainly from Harvard University and the Massachusetts Institute of Technology. So fresh was it that we find him using, at the outset, with apparent ease his calculus—both differential and integral—tools that have a habit of losing edge with disuse. Physically, also, he had a qualification of great importance for the special work he was to undertake, — that of perceiving on the disks of the planets, very fine markings close to the limit of visibility; for the late Dr. Hasket Derby, then the leading practitioner in Ophthalmology in Boston, told Professor Julian Coolidge that Percival's eyesight was the keenest he had ever examined.

One essential remained, to find the best atmosphere for his purpose. In entering our air the rays of light from the stars are deflected, that is bent, and bent again when they strike a denser or less dense stratum. But these strata are continually changing with currents of warmer or colder air rising and falling above the surface of the earth, and hence the rays of light are being shifted a little from side to side as they reach us. Everyone is familiar with the twinkling of the stars, caused in this way; for before entering our atmosphere their light is perfectly steady. Moreover, everyone must have observed that the amount of twinkling varies greatly. At times it is unusually intense, and at others the stars seem wonderfully still. Now, although the planets, being near enough to show a disk visible through a telescope, do not seem to twinkle, the same thing in fact occurs. The light is deflected, and the shaking makes it very difficult to see the smaller markings. Imagine trying to make out the detail on an elaborately decorated plate held up by a man with a palsied hand. The plate would be seen easily, but for the detail one would wish it held in a steadier grasp, and for observing the planets this corresponds to a steadier atmosphere.

Percival's own account of the reason for his expedition of 1894 to observe the planet Mars, why he selected Flagstaff as the site, what he did there and how the plan developed into the permanent observatory that bears his name were told in what was intended to be an introduction to the first volume of the Annals of the Observatory. Perhaps owing to the author's illness in the last years of the century this statement was mislaid and was not found until February 22, 1901. It is here printed in full.

Annals of the Lowell Observatory

INTRODUCTION

In the summer of 1877 occurred an event which was to mark a new departure in astronomy,—the detection by Schiaparelli of the so-called canals of the planet Mars. The detection of these markings has led to the turning over of an entirely new page in cosmogony.

Schiaparelli's discovery shared the fate of all important astronomical advances,—even Newton's theory of gravitation was duly combatted in its day,—it, and still more the possibilities with which it was fraught, distanced the comprehension of its time. In consequence, partly from general disbelief, partly from special difficulty, no notable addition was made to Schiaparelli's own work until 1892, when Professor W. H. Pickering attacked the planet at the Boyden Station of the Harvard Observatory at Arequipa, Peru, and made the next addition to our knowledge of our neighbor world.

Intrinsically important as was Pickering's work, it was even more important extrinsically. Schiaparelli's discoveries were due solely to the genius of the man,—his insight, not his eyesight, for at the telescope eyes differ surprisingly little, brains surprisingly much; Pickering's brought into coöperation a practically new instrument, the air itself. For at the same time with his specific advance came a general one,—the realization of the supreme importance of atmosphere in astronomical research. To the Harvard Observatory is due the first really far-reaching move in this direction, and to Professor W. H. Pickering of that observatory the first fruits in carrying it out.

It was at this stage in our knowledge of the possibilities in planetary work and of the means to that end, in the winter of 1893-94, that the writer determined to make an expedition which included the putting up of an observatory for the primary purpose of studying, under the best pro-

curable conditions, the planet Mars at his then coming opposition,—an opposition at which the planet, though not
quite so close to us as in 1892, would be better placed for
northern observers. In this expedition he associated with
himself Prof. W. H. Pickering and Mr. A. E. Douglass.

The writer had two objects in view:

1st, the determination of the physical condition of the
planets of our solar system, primarily Mars;

2d, the determination of the conditions conducive to the
best astronomical observations.

How vital was the inter-connection of the two was demonstrated by the results.

Important as atmosphere is to any astronomical investigation, it is all-important to the study of the planets. To get,
therefore, within the limits of the United States—limits at
the time for several reasons advisable—as steady air as possible, Prof. W. H. Pickering, who had already had experience
of Southern California as well as of Arequipa, Peru, proposed Arizona as the most promising spot. Accordingly,
Mr. A. E. Douglass left Boston in March, 1894, with a six-inch
Clark refractor belonging to the writer, to make a test of the
seeing throughout the Territory. From his report, Flagstaff
was selected for the observatory site.

Flagstaff, then a town of eight hundred inhabitants, lies
on the line of the Atlantic and Pacific Railroad, in the centre
of the great plateau of northern Arizona, half way across
the Territory from east to west, and two fifths way down
from north to south. This plateau, whose mean elevation
is between 6000 and 7000 feet, is a great pine oasis a hundred
miles or more in diameter, rising some 3000 feet from out
the Arizona desert. It culminates in the mass known as the

San Francisco Peaks, ten miles north of Flagstaff, whose highest summit rises 12,872 feet above the level of the sea.[1]

The spot chosen was the eastern edge of the mesa (table-land) to the west of Flagstaff. The site lay open to the east and south, and was shielded on the north by the San Francisco Peaks. The distance from the observatory to Mt. Agassiz, the most conspicuous of the Peaks from the Flagstaff side, was about eight miles and three fifths in an airline, and the distance to the town about a mile and a quarter. As soon as the site was selected, the town very kindly deeded to the observatory a piece of land and built a road up to it.

The observatory stood 350 feet above the town, and 7250 feet above the level of the sea, in latitude 35° 11′ north and longitude 111° 40′ west.

Prof. W. H. Pickering, to whose skill and ability was chiefly due the successful setting up of the observatory, suggested arrangements with Brashear for the use of an eighteen-inch refractor which Brashear had recently constructed,—the largest glass to be had at the time,—arrangements which were accordingly made. He then devised and superintended the construction of a dome intended to be of a temporary character, which worked admirably. The upper part of it was made in sections in Cambridgeport, Mass., and then shipped West, the lower part being constructed according to his specifications on the spot, under the superintendence of Mr. Douglass.

The telescope was supported on one of the Clark mountings. The bed-plate, clock-work, and a twelve-inch telescope were leased of the Harvard College Observatory, and the

---

[1] The exact elevation proved to be 12,611.

mounting then altered by Alvan Clark & Sons to carry both the twelve and the eighteen-inch telescopes.

Six weeks from the time ground was broken, on April 23, 1894, regular observations with the eighteen-inch were begun.

The results of the year's work surpassed anticipation. Details invisible at the average observatory were presented at times with copper-plate distinctness, and, what is as vital, the markings were seen hour after hour, day after day, month after month. First sight; then system; and the one of these factors was as fundamental to the results as the other. Systematic work, first made possible and then properly performed, was the open sesame to that most difficult branch of astronomical observations, the study of our nearest neighbors in the universe.

The chief results obtained were:—

1st, the detection of the physical characteristics of the planet Mars to a degree of completeness sufficient to permit of the forming of a general theory of its condition, revealing beyond reasonable doubt first its general habitability, and second its particular habitation at the present moment by some form of local intelligence;

2d, corroboration and extension by Professor Pickering of his discoveries at Arequipa with regard to the forms of Jupiter's Satellites;[2]

3d, the discovery and study by Mr. Douglass of the atmospheric causes upon which good seeing depends.

It is of the observations connected with the first of these that the present volume of the Annals alone treats.

As the publication of this volume has been so long delayed,

[2] These discoveries have since been doubted.

it seems fitting to add here a brief continuation of the history of the observatory to the present time.

The results of the expedition in 1894, in the detection of planetary detail, turned out to be so important an advance upon what had previously been accomplished that the writer decided to form of the temporary expedition a permanent observatory. Accordingly, he had Alvan Clark & Sons make him a twenty-four-inch refractor, which fate decided should be their last large glass; the Yerkes glass, although not yet in operation at the time this goes to press, having been finished at nearly the time his was begun. The glass received from Mantois happened to be singularly flawless and its working the same. It was made twenty-four inches in clear aperture, and of a focal length of thirty-one feet. Alvan G. Clark accompanied the writer to Flagstaff and put the glass in place himself.

The mounting for the telescope was likewise made by the Clarks. Rigidity was the prime essential, in order to secure as stable an image as possible, and this has been admirably carried out, the mounting being the heaviest and most stable for a glass of its size yet made.

In July, 1896, Dr. T. J. J. See joined the observatory, to continue there the line of research for which he was already well known—the study of the double stars. This added to the two initial objects of the observatory a third,—

3d, the study of double-star systems, including a complete catalogue of those in the southern heavens.

During the summer and autumn of 1896 the importance of good atmosphere was further demonstrated in an interesting and somewhat surprising quarter. The air by day was found to be as practicable as that by night. While Mars was being studied by night, the study of Venus and Mercury was taken up during the daytime systematically, and the results proved as significant as had been those on Mars. Instead of the vague diffused patches hitherto commonly recorded, both planets' surfaces turned out to be diversified by markings of so distinct a character as not only to disclose their rotation periods but to furnish the fundamental facts of the physical conditions of their surfaces. We know now more about Mercury and Venus than we previously knew of Mars.

As the winter in Flagstaff is not so good as the summer, it was thought well to try Mexico during that season of the year. Accordingly, a new dome was made; the telescope was taken down; and dome, mounting, and glasses were carried to Mexico and set up for the winter at Tacubaya, a suburb of the City of Mexico, at an elevation of 7500 feet. There the observatory received every kindness at the hands of the President, the Government, and the National Observatory.

Observations at Mexico fully corroborated those at Flagstaff with regard to both Mars, Mercury and Venus, and enabled Mr. Douglass to make the first full determination of the markings on Jupiter's third and fourth satellites, thus fixing their rotation periods.

Dr. See in the mean time, who while at Flagstaff had discovered a very large number of new doubles, in Mexico added to his list; . . .

With the spring the observatory was shipped back again to Flagstaff.

Of the particular results in planetary work obtained, several papers have been published in various astronomical

journals, while of them subsequent volumes of the Annals
will speak in detail. In the meantime two general conclusions to which they have led the writer may, as possessing
future interest, fittingly be mentioned here:

1st, that the physical condition of the various members
of our solar system appears to be such as evolution from
a primal nebula would demand;

2d, that what we call life is an inevitable detail of cosmic
evolution, as inherent a property of matter from an eventual
standpoint as gravitation itself is from an instant one: as a
primal nebula or meteoric swarm, actuated by purely natural
laws, evolves a system of bodies, so each body under the same
laws, conditioned only by size and position, inevitably
evolves upon itself organic forms.

The reasons for the first of these conclusions have sprung
directly from the writer's study of the several members of
our own solar system; his reason for the second, upon the
further facts,—

1st, that where the physical conditions upon these bodies
point to the apparent possibility of life, we find apparent
signs of life;

2d, where they do not, we find none.

This implies that, however much its detail may vary, life is
essentially the same everywhere, since we can reason apparently correctly as to its presence or absence, a result which
is in striking accord with the spectroscopic evidence of a practical identity of material.

Evidently the expedition to observe Mars was undertaken
quite suddenly, but if it was to be made at all it must be done
quickly. Anyone, however unfamiliar with astronomy, will

perceive that two planets revolving about the sun in independent orbits will be nearest together when they are on the same side of the sun and farthest apart when on opposite sides of it, and that the difference is especially great if, as in the case of the earth and Mars, their orbits are not far apart, for when on the same side the separation is only the difference of their distances from the sun, and when on opposite sides it is the sum of those distances. Moreover, Mars being outside of the Earth its whole face is seen in the full light of the sun when both bodies are on the same side of it. Now such a condition, called opposition, was to occur in the summer after Percival's return from Japan, and therefore there was no time to spare in getting an observatory ready for use.

From the experience of others elsewhere, Percival was convinced that the most favorable atmospheric situations would lie in one of the two desert bands that encircle a great part of the Earth, north and south of the equator, caused by the sucking up of moisture by the trade winds; and that a mountain, with the currents of air running up and down it, did not offer so steady an atmosphere as a high table-land. The height is important because the amount of atmosphere through which the light travels is much less than at sea level. He was aware that the best position of this kind might well be found in some foreign country; but again there was no time to search for it, or indeed to build an observatory far away, if it must be equipped by the early summer. The fairly dry and high plateau of northern Arizona seemed, therefore, to offer the best chance of a favorable site for this immediate and temporary expedition.

With the aid of suggestions by Professor William H.

Pickering, who knew what was needed in observing Mars, he sent Mr. Douglass, with the six-inch telescope brought back from Japan, to Arizona to inspect the astronomic steadiness of the atmosphere. The instructions, apparently drawn up by Professor Pickering, were dated February 28th, directing him to observe on two nights each at Tombstone, Tucson and Phoenix; and Percival, keeping in constant touch with Mr. Douglass by letter and telegraph, added among other places Flagstaff. This was shortly followed by instructions about constructing the circular vertical part of the dome for the observatory by local contract as soon as the site was selected, while the spherical part above, which was to be of parallel arches covered with wire netting and canvas, was being made in the East and to be shipped shortly. Meanwhile the pier was being built by Alvan Clark & Sons (who had made most of the large telescopes in this country) and the mounting for both the eighteen-inch and the twelve-inch telescope thereon, balancing each other. Mr. Douglass was to report constantly; and in April Percival wrote him to take a photograph of the site of the observatory "now," then every day as the work progressed, and have the negatives developed, a blue print made of each as speedily as possible and sent East. All this is stated here to show the speed, and at the same time the careful thought, with which the work was done. Percival and his colleagues came as near as possible to carrying out the principle, "when you have made up your mind that a thing must be done, and done quickly, do it yesterday."

In fact Percival did not select any of the three places first examined, but on consideration of Mr. Douglass' reports preferred Flagstaff; and his choice has been abundantly confirmed by the pioneering problems undertaken there, and by the fact that this site was retained for the later permanent Observatory. Everyone, indeed, deserves much credit for the rapid work done at such a distance from principals busy with the preparation of the instruments. It was characteristic of Percival that he got the very best out of those who worked with and under him.

Although the closest point of the opposition did not occur until the autumn, the two planets, travelling in the same direction, were near enough together for fair observation some months earlier; and on May 28th, arriving at Flagstaff, Percival writes to his mother: "Here on the day. Telescope ready for use tonight for its Arizonian virgin view. . . . After lunch all to the observatory where carpenters were giving their finishing touches. . . . Today has been cloudy but now shows signs of a beautiful night and so, not to bed, but to post and then to gaze." The sky was not clear that night, for an unprecedented rain came and lasted several days, falling through the still uncanvased dome on Professor Pickering and Percival, who had been lured by a "fairing" sky into camping out there in the evening to be on time for the early rising Mars. But it was not long before the weather cleared and the strenuous work began. As the observatory was a mile and a half from the hotel in the town, and up-hill, it was uncomfortable to arrive there at three o'clock in the morning, the hour when at that season Mars came in sight. So in the summer a cottage was built hard by the dome, where they could sleep and get their meals.

The observations were, of course, continuous throughout the rest of the year; and except for two trips East on business, one for a few weeks at the end of June, another in September, and a few days in Los Angeles, Percival was there all the time. As usual he worked furiously; for beside observing most of the night he spent much of the day writing reports and papers, making drawings for publication in scientific and other periodicals, and investigating collateral questions that bore upon their significance; and while he had computers for mechanical detail, he and his colleagues had to prepare and supervise their work. To his mother he wrote, as a rule, every day; and in some of these letters he gave an account of his time. On September 2nd, he writes of being up the greater part of the night, and naturally perpetually sleepy. "But the number of canals increases encouragingly— in the Lake of the Sun region we have seen nearly all Schiaparelli's and about as many more." On October 10th: "Observed the better part of last night, after being welcomed by everybody—and have been as a busy as a beaver today, writing an article, drawing for ditto etc, etc."; and, two days later, "Chock full of work; scrabbling each day for the post—proof etc. Mr. Douglass is now on the hill observing Mercury. We all dine there at seven. Then I take Mars and at 3 A.M. Professor Pickering, Jupiter. So you see none of the planets are neglected."

In one of these letters he encloses a clipping from a San Francisco newspaper satirizing Professor Holden for saying that the canals of Mars reported at Flagstaff were not confirmed by observations at Mount Hamilton. Denial or doubt that he had really seen what—after many observations confirmed by those of his colleagues—he reported as seen always vexed Percival, and naturally so. Yet they were not uncommon and sometimes attributed to defective vision. He was well aware that while a belief that a thing exists may make

one think he has seen it when he has not, yet it is also true
that one person perfectly familiar with an object sought will
find it when another, unacquainted with its precise appearance, will miss it altogether. Everyone knows that people in
the habit of looking for four-leaved clovers are constantly
picking them while others never see them; or that a skilled
archaeologist finds arrowheads with much greater facility
than a tyro, who will, however, improve rapidly with a little
experience; and all this is especially true of things near the
very limit of visibility. Gradually more and more observers
began to see the finer markings and the canals on Mars, until finally the question of their existence was set at rest when
it became possible to photograph them.

But in spite of work and vexation the life was far from
dull, for the observatory was as hospitable as its limited
quarters would allow. Visitors were attracted by its growing
reputation, and on August 25th he writes: "Just as we were
plodding up there last evening in the dark we heard a car-
riage-full of folk coming down. We suspected what they had
been after and were not surprised when they challenged us
with 'Are you observatory people?' It seems they were, as
they informed us pathetically, people from the East and
had gone up to look through the glass, if they might, before
taking the train at 12.30 that night. Of course we could not
resist their appeals and so, though we had thought to turn
in betimes because of early observations in the morning,
entertained these angels—half of them were women—on
'just like diamonds' as they said of the stars. The out-of-
focus views pleased them the most—as turns out to be the
case generally. This morning when I went to take Pickering's place I found another angel in the shape of a Colorado

man, out here for his health, in the dome with Pickering—a nice fellow he turned out. It was then 4 h. 8 m. o'clock in the morning,—a matutinal hour for a man to trudge a mile and a half on no breakfast up to an observatory on a hill— That shows real astronomical interest. He was rewarded gastronomically with some coffee of my brewing, all three of us breakfasting standing by the platform."

There were occasional picnics and trips to the cave dwellings, the Grand Cañon, the petrified forest and other sights. Moreover, Percival greatly enjoyed the scenery about Flagstaff, and took an interest in the people of the town, although well aware of inexperience in some matters. On October 13th he says: "There was a grand republican rally last night and the young Flagstaff band that is learning to play in tune serenaded the speaker of the occasion under the hotel windows in fine style. When you knew the air beforehand you could follow it with enthusiasm."

CHAPTER X

MARS

MEANWHILE the work of the Observatory went on, partly in the direction of the special lines of the several observers, but mainly in that of the founder whose interest was then predominantly planetary, especially in Mars; and from this the site of the dome came to be called Mars Hill. The clear atmosphere yielded the results that had been hoped for, and much was discovered about the planets, their period of rotation, satellites etc., but above all were the Martian observations fruitful. There the object was to watch the seasonal changes beginning with the vernal equinox, or spring of the southern hemisphere, the one inclined toward the earth when the two bodies approach most closely, and follow them through the summer and autumn of our neighbor. For those not familiar with the topography of Mars it may be said that the greater part of its surface is a reddish or orange color interspersed with patches or broken bands of a blue, or greenish blue, in the southern temperate zone. These had been supposed to be seas, and are still known by names recalling that opinion, while the lighter regions derived their nomenclature from the theory that they are continents or islands standing out of the water. This is confusing, but must be borne in mind by anyone who looks at a map of the planet and tries to understand the meaning of the terms. There are several reasons for thinking that the dark areas are not seas: one that they change in depth of color with the seasons; another that light reflected from water is polarized and in this case it is not; also they never show a brilliant specular reflection of the Sun as seas would do.

Now in the winter of the Martian southern hemisphere the region around that pole turned white, that is it became covered by a mantle appearing like snow or ice, and as the summer advanced this became less and less until it disappeared altogether. Meanwhile there formed around it a dark mass that spread downwards, toward the temperate zone and into the bluish areas there, which assumed a darker hue. After the deepening color had reached the edge of the wrongly called sea, very thin straight lines appeared proceeding from it into the lighter reddish regions (mistaken for continents) toward the equator, and increased rapidly in number until there was a great network of them. It very often happened that more than two of these intersected at the same point, and when that occurred there usually came a distinct dot much larger than the thickness of the lines themselves. After this process was fairly under way the dark areas faded down again, and then similar fine lines appeared in them, connecting with those in the light areas, and apparently continuing toward the pole. Moreover, some of the lines in the light region doubled, that is two parallel lines appeared usually running in this case not to the centres, but to the two sides of the dark dots. It is essential to add that the limit of thickness for any line on Mars to be seen by their telescopes was estimated at about fifteen miles, so that these fine lines must have been at least of that width.

Such is in brief the outline of that which the observers saw. What did these things mean? What was the interpretation of the phenomena, their opinion on the causes and operation.? This, with the details of the observations, is given by Percival in his book "Mars," written immediately after this first year of observation, the preface bearing the date November, 1895. But it must not be supposed that he started to observe with any preconceived idea that the planet was inhabited, or with the object of proving that the so-called canals were the work of intelligent beings, for in the preface to the fourth edition he says: "The theory contained in this book was conceived by me toward the end of the first year's work at Flagstaff. Up to that time, although the habitability of Mars had been often suggested and strenuously opposed, no theory based upon sufficient facts had ever been put forth that bound the facts into a logical consistent whole—the final rivet perhaps was when the idea of the oases occurred to me." The oases were the dots at the intersection of the fine lines which were called by Schiaparelli "canali" and have retained the name canals.

"Mars" begins with a description of the planet, of its orbit, size and shape, as compared with that of the Earth. By means of its trifling satellites its mass was determined, and from this and its dimensions the force of gravity at its surface, which was found to be a little over one third of that on the Earth; so that living creatures, if any, could be much larger than those of the same type here. From the markings that could be seen on its face the period of rotation, that is the length of the Martian day, was measured with great accuracy, being about forty minutes longer than our own; while the Martian year, known from its revolution round the sun, was about twice the length of ours. All this led to a calculation of the nature of the planet's seasons, which for its southern

.hemisphere—the one turned toward the Earth when the two
bodies are near together as in 1894—gave a long cold winter
and a summer short and hot.

He then takes up the question of atmosphere, which, with
water, is absolutely necessary for life, and even for physical
changes of any kind "when once what was friable had
crumbled to pieces under the alternate roasting and refrig-
erating, relatively speaking, to which the body's surface
would be exposed as it turned round on its axis into and out
of the sun's rays. Such disintegration once accomplished, the
planet would roll thenceforth a mummy world through
space," like our own moon, as he says, where, except for
the possible tumbling in of a crater wall, all is now deathly
still. But on Mars changes occur on a scale vast enough
to be visible from the Earth, and he tells in greater detail the
first of those noted in the preceding summary, the formation
and melting of the polar snows. Moreover, a change was observed in the diameter of the planet, which could be explained
only by the presence of a twilight zone, and this meant an
atmosphere refracting the rays of the sun, a phenomenon
that he dwells upon at some length. He then turns to the
nature of the atmosphere, and from the relative cloudless-
ness and the lesser force of gravity concludes that its density
is probably about one seventh of that on the surface of the
Earth. So much for its quantity. For its quality he considers
the kinetic theory of gases, and calculates that in spite of
its lesser gravity it could retain oxygen, nitrogen, water
vapor, and in fact all the elements of our atmosphere.

He next considers the question of water, the other essential
to the existence of life, animal or vegetable; the phenomenon
of the diminution, and final disappearance, of the polar

cap, the behavior of the dark blue band which formed along it; and says: "That the blue was water at the edge of the melting snow seems unquestionable. That it was the color of water; that it so persistently bordered the melting snow; and that it subsequently vanished, are three facts mutually confirmatory to this deduction. But a fourth bit of proof, due to the ingenuity of Professor W. H. Pickering, adds its weight to the other three. For he made the polariscope tell the same tale. On scrutinizing the great bay through an Arago polariscope, he found the light coming from the bay to be polarized. Now, to polarize the light it reflects is a property, as we know, of a smooth surface such as that of water is." The great bay of which he speaks is the widest part of the blue band. He discusses the suggestion that the white cap is due, as had been suggested, to congealed carbonic acid gas instead of ice or snow from water, and points out that with the slight density of the Martian atmosphere this would require a degree of cold impossible under the conditions of the planet; an important conclusion later fully confirmed by radiometric measures at Flagstaff and Mt. Wilson.

Assuming therefore that the polar cap is composed of snow or ice, he traced its history, as observed more closely than ever before at Flagstaff, and gives a map of its gradual shrinking and final disappearance, with the corresponding condition of the blue water at its edge. All this from June 3 to October 13 of our year, or from May 1 to July 13 of the Martian seasons, and this was the first time the cap had been seen to vanish wholly. It is interesting to note that in the early morning of June 8 "as I was watching the planet, I saw suddenly two points like stars flash out in the midst of the polar cap. Dazzlingly bright upon the duller white background of the snow, these stars shone for a few moments and then slowly disappeared. The seeing at the time was very good. It is at once evident what the other-world apparitions were,—not the fabled signal lights of Martian folk, but the glint of ice-slopes flashing for a moment earthward as the rotation of the planet turned the slope to the proper angle . . . nine minutes before they reach Earth they had ceased to be on Mars, and, after their travel of one hundred millions of miles, found to note them but one watcher, alone on a hill-top with the dawn."

Seven years before Green, at Madeira, had seen the same thing at the same spot on the planet, drawn the same conclusion, and named the heights the Mitchell Mountains, after the man who had done the like in 1846. Later the blue belt below the cap turned brown; "of that mud-color land does from which the water has recently been drained off," and at last, "where the polar ice-cap and polar sea had been was now one ochre stretch of desert."

The geography of Mars he describes, but what he tells cannot be made intelligible without the twelve successive views he gives of the planet as it turns around; while the names of places, given in the main by Schiaparelli, are based in large part on the mistaken impression that the dark regions were seas and bays, the light ones continents and islands. "Previous to the present chart," Percival writes, "the most detailed map of the planet was Schiaparelli's, made in 1888. On comparison with his, it will be seen that the present one substantially confirms all his detail, and adds to it about as much more. I have adopted his nomenclature, and in the naming of the newly found features have selected names conformable to his scheme, which commends itself both on practical and on poetic grounds." By this, of course, he does not mean to commend naming the dark areas as seas, for his description of the features on the planet's surface is followed by a statement of the reasons, apparently conclusive, for assuming that the blue-green regions cannot be seas, but must be vegetation; while the reddish ochre ones are simply desert.

"Upon the melting of its polar cap, and the transference of the water thus annually set free to go its rounds, seem to depend all the seasonal phenomena on the surface of the planet.

"The observations upon which this deduction is based extend over a period of nearly six months, from the last day of May to the 22d of November. They cover the regions from the south pole to about latitude forty north. That changes analogous to those recorded, differing, however, in details, occur six Martian months later in the planet's northern hemisphere, is proved by what Schiaparelli has seen." In order that the reader may not be confused, and wonder why the changes at the north pole do not begin shortly after those in the southern hemisphere are over, he must remember that the Martian year has 687 days, and is thus nearly twice as long as ours, or in other words that the period of these observations covered only about four months in Mars.

"So soon as the melting of the snow was well under way, long straits, of deeper tint than their surroundings, made their appearance in the midst of the dark areas," although the dark areas were then at their darkest. "For some time the dark areas continued largely unchanged in appearance; that is, during the earlier and most extensive melting of the

snow-cap. After this their history became one long chronicle
of fading out. Their lighter parts grew lighter, and their
darker ones less dark. For, to start with, they were made
up of many tints; various shades of blue-green interspersed
with glints of orange-yellow. . . . Toward the end of October, a strange, and, for observational purposes, a distressing
phenomenon took place. What remained of the more southern dark regions showed a desire to vanish, so completely did
those regions proceed to fade in tint throughout." He points
out that such a change is inexplicable if the dark areas were
water, for there was no place for it to go to. "But if, instead
of being due to water, the blue-green tint had been due to
leaves and grasses, just such a fading out as was observed
should have taken place as autumn came on, and that without
proportionate increase of green elsewhere; for the great
continental areas, being desert, are incapable of supporting
vegetation, and therefore of turning green." By the continental areas he meant the barren regions, formerly thought
to stand out from seas in contrast with the darker ones supposed to be water.

"Thus we see that several independent phenomena all
agree to show that the blue-green regions of Mars are not
water, but, generally at least, areas of vegetation; from
which it follows that Mars is very badly off for water, and
that the planet is dependent on the melting of its polar
snows for practically its whole supply.

"Such scarcity of water on Mars is just what theory would
lead us to expect. Mars is a smaller planet than the Earth,
and therefore is relatively more advanced in his evolutionary
career." And as a planet grows old its water retreats through
cracks and caverns into its interior. The so-called seas were,

he thinks, once such, and "are still the lowest portions of the planet, and therefore stand to receive what scant water may yet travel over the surface." With this agrees the fact that the divisions between the dark and light areas run south-east north-west; as they would if made by currents in water flowing from the pole toward the equator.

"Now, if a planet were at any stage of its career able to support life, it is probable that a diminishing water supply would be the beginning of the end of that life, for the air would outlast the available water.[1] . . .

"Mars is, apparently, in this distressing plight at the present moment, the signs being that its water supply is now exceedingly low. If, therefore, the planet possess inhabitants, there is but one course open to them in order to support life. Irrigation, and upon as vast a scale as possible, must be the all-engrossing Martian pursuit. . . .

"At this point in our inquiry, when direct deduction from the general physical phenomena observable on the planet's surface shows that, were there inhabitants there, a system of irrigation would be an all-essential of their existence, the telescope presents us with perhaps the most startling discovery of modern times,—the so-called canals of Mars."

He then takes up these so-called canals or lines which start from the edge of the blue-green regions, proceed directly to what seem centres in the middle of the ochre areas, where they meet other lines that come, he says, "with apparently a like determinate intent. And this state of things is not confined to any one part of the planet, but takes place all

[1] The theory of the gradual loss of water is very doubtful, but Percival's main conclusions depend on the present aridity of the planet, not on its assumed history.

over the reddish-ochre regions," that is the arid belt of the planet. "Plotting upon a globe betrays them to be arcs of great circles almost invariably, even the few outstanding exceptions seeming to be but polygonal combinations of the same." These two facts, that the lines are great circles, or the shortest distance between points on the surface of the planet, and that several of them often meet at the same place, must be borne in mind, because they are essential elements in his argument that they are the result of an intelligent plan.

The lines are of enormous length, the shortest being 250 miles, and the longest 3,540, and at times three, four, five, and even seven come together at one spot. By them the whole region is cut up, and how many there may be cannot now, he says, be determined, for the better the air at the observatory the more of them become visible. At Flagstaff they detected 183, seen from once to 127 times, and there were in the aggregate 3,240 records made of them.[2]

In seeking for the origin of the lines he begins by discarding natural causation on the ground first of their straightness, and second of their uniform width, regularities not to be found to any such a degree in the processes of nature. His third ground is "that the lines form a system; that, instead of running anywhither, they join certain points to certain others, making thus, not a simple network, but one whose meshes connect centres directly with one another. . . . If lines be drawn haphazard over the surface of a globe, the chances are ever so many to one against more than two lines crossing each other at any point. Simple crossings of two lines will of course be common in something like factorial

[2] In a lecture shortly before his death he said: "Where Schiaparelli discovered 140, between 700 and 800 have been detected at Flagstaff."

proportion to the number of lines; but that any other line should contrive to cross at the same point would be a coincidence whose improbability only a mathematician can properly appreciate, so very great is it. . . . In other words, we might search in vain for a single instance of such encounter. On the surface of Mars, however, instead of searching in vain, we find the thing occurring *passim;* this *a priori* most improbable rendezvousing proving the rule, not the exception. Of the crossings that are best seen, all are meeting places for more than two canals."

He then takes up the question of cracks radiating from centres of explosion or fissure, and points out that such cracks would not be of uniform breadth. There are cracks on the moon which look like cracks, while the lines on Mars do not. Moreover, the lines fit into one another which would not be true of cracks radiating from different centres. The lines cannot be rivers for those would not be the same width throughout, or run on arcs of great circles. Nor can the lines be furrows ploughed by meteorites, since these would not run straight from one centre to another; in short the objection from the infinitesimal chance of several lines crossing at the same point applies. "In truth," he concludes, "no natural theory has yet been advanced which will explain these lines."

The development, or order in the visibility, of the canals throws light on their nature. Early in the Martian spring they were invisible, then those nearest to the melting snows of its south pole appeared, and in a general succession those farther and farther away; but when they did appear they were always in the same place where they had been seen before. Each canal, however, did not darken all at once, but gradually; and this he accounts for by saying that what we see is not water but vegetation which takes time to develop. "If, therefore, we suppose what we call a canal to be, not the canal proper, but the vegetation along its banks, the observed phenomena stand accounted for. This suggestion was first made some years ago by Professor W. H. Pickering.

"That what we see is not the canal proper, but the line of land it irrigates, disposes incidentally of the difficulty of conceiving a canal several miles wide. On the other hand, a narrow, fertilized strip of country is what we should expect to find; for, as we have seen, the general physical condition of the planet leads us to the conception, not of canals constructed for waterways,—like our Suez Canal,—but of canals dug for irrigation purposes. We cannot, of course, be sure that such is their character, appearances being often highly deceitful; we can only say that, so far, the supposition best explains what we see. Further details of their development point to this same conclusion." Such as that with time they darken rather than broaden.

To the objection that canals could not be built in straight lines because of mountain ranges he replies that the surface of Mars is surprisingly flat, and this he proves by careful observations of the terminator, that is the edge of that part of the planet lighted by the Sun, where any considerable sudden changes of elevation on the surface of the planet would appear, and do not.

He then tells of the discovery by Mr. Douglass of the canals in the dark regions toward the south pole. They could not be seen while those regions remained dark, but when they faded out the canals became visible, and supplied the missing link explaining how the water from the melting polar cap was conveyed to the canals in the arid space north and south of the equator. Mr. Douglass found no less than forty-four of them, almost all of which he saw more than once, one on as many as thirty-seven occasions.

Then came the phenomenon that convinced Percival of an artificial system of irrigation: "Dotted all over the reddish-ochre ground of the desert stretches of the planet . . . are an innumerable number of dark circular or oval spots. They appear, furthermore, always in intimate association with the canals. They constitute so many hubs to which the canals make spokes"; and there is not a single instance of such a spot, unconnected by a canal, and by more than one, with the rest of the system. These spots are in general circular, from 120 to 150 miles in diameter, and make their appearance after, but not long after, the canals that lead to them, those that appear first becoming after a time less conspicuous, those seen later more so. In short they behave as oases of vegetation would when a supply of water had reached them, and thus give "an end and object for the existence of canals, and the most natural one in the world, namely, that the canals are constructed for the express purpose of fertilizing the oases. . . . This, at least, is the only explanation that fully accounts for the facts. Of course all such evidence of design may be purely fortuitous, with about as much probability, as it has happily been put, as that a chance collection of numbers should take the form of the multiplication table." He does not fail to point out that great circles for the canals, and circular shapes for the oases, are the forms most economical if artificially constructed; nor does his reasoning rest upon a small number of instances, for up to the close of

observations at that time fifty-three oases had been discovered.

Finally he deals with the corroborating phenomena of
double canals and the curious dark spots where the canals in
the dark regions debouch into those that run through the
deserts.

In his conclusion he sums up his ideas as follows:

"To review, now, the chain of reasoning by which we have
been led to regard it probable that upon the surface of Mars
we see the effects of local intelligence. We find, in the first
place, that the broad physical conditions of the planet are
not antagonistic to some form of life; secondly, that there is
an apparent dearth of water upon the planet's surface, and
therefore, if beings of sufficient intelligence inhabited it, they
would have to resort to irrigation to support life; thirdly,
that there turns out to be a network of markings covering
the disk precisely counterparting what a system of irrigation
would look like; and, lastly, that there is a set of spots placed
where we should expect to find the lands thus artificially
fertilized, and behaving as such constructed oases should.
All this, of course, may be a set of coincidences, signifying
nothing; but the probability points the other way."

Such was the harvest of facts and ideas garnered from
Mars at the Observatory during this summer of tireless
watching. Both the facts and the conclusions drawn from
them were received with incredulity by astronomers whose
atmospheres and unfamiliarity with the things to be observed hindered their seeing the phenomena, and to whom
the explanations seemed fantastic. With more careful observation skepticism about the phenomena decreased, one
observer after another seeing the change of color on the

planet, the growth of vegetation, and in some form the lines and the dots, although many skilled observers still see them as irregular markings rather than as fine uniform lines. The hypothesis of artificial construction of the canals by intelligent beings has met with much more resistance. It runs against the blade of Occam's razor, that nothing should be attributed to conscious intelligent action unless it cannot be explained by natural forces. Percival seems to have made a very strong argument against any natural cause yet suggested, and a rational case for an intelligent agency if no natural one can be found. There, for the present, his hypothesis may be said to rest.

The favorable period for observation during the opposition of Mars having come to an end, the two larger telescopes, which had been hired or borrowed for the expedition, were returned in the spring to their owners, the observatory at Flagstaff being dismantled, and the rest of the apparatus brought East and stored; but plans for further work on Mars were by no means given up; and Percival—bent on still better equipment for the next opposition of Mars, in the summer of 1896—arranged with Alvan Clark & Sons for the manufacture of a 24-inch refractor lens. The Clarks were then the most successful makers of large lenses in the world; for up to that time it had not been possible to cast and cool these large pieces of glass so that they were perfectly uniform in density, and the art of the Clarks consisted in grinding and rubbing the surface so as to make its slight departure from the calculated curves compensate for any unevenness in density; and to a less extent it is still necessary. It required a skill of eye and hand unequalled elsewhere, and Percivals' lens was one of the most perfect they ever made.

Where the telescope should be set up was not yet decided; for it will be remembered that he wanted to make his observations in any accessible place in the world where the clearest, and especially the steadiest, atmosphere would be found. As already explained, he believed this lay in one of the two great desert belts that encircle the Earth north and south of the equator; and, for practical purposes, that meant Arizona, Mexico and South America in the Western Hemisphere, and the Sahara in the Eastern. Mr. Douglass had therefore been sent—probably with the faithful 6-inch telescope—to Mexico and South America, while Percival proposed to examine the Sahara himself.

CHAPTER XI

THE PERMANENT OBSERVATORY—
INTERLUDES AND TRAVELS

THE year following his return to Boston, at the end of November, 1894, was filled with the arrangements for his new telescope and apparatus, and in writing the book on Mars. At this time he lived at 11 West Cedar Street, the little house he had bought some time before; for it was characteristic that, while lavishing whatever was needed on his observatory, he was modest in his expenditure on himself. By the end of the year his book was published, his work for the coming observatory was done, and he went to Europe; but his Mother had died in March, and the daily stream of loving letters, which told about himself, had ceased to flow.

On December 10, 1895, he sailed on the *Spree* with Alvan G. Clark, the last surviving brother of the telescope-making family. The voyage, though very rough at times, was uneventful, until as they were entering the Solent the vessel struck, and stuck fast, on Warden's Ledge, just inside the Needles. "Fault of the pilot" Percival recorded, "aged 73 and bordering on imbecility." With all his travels about and around the world this is the nearest he ever came to shipwreck; nor was it for him very near, for since the ship could not get herself clear tugs came down the next day and took off the passengers, who were landed at Southampton and went up to London. Two days later he was in Paris, and for nearly three weeks he and Clark saw astronomical friends,—among others having to lunch and dinner Edouard Mantois, the great glass manufacturer who had cast the new 24-inch refractor for his telescope. Percival enjoyed a most interesting dinner at the house of Flammarion, the astronomer and novelist, who was devoted to Mars and had followed his work at Flagstaff. As he wrote to his Father— "There were fourteen of us, and all that could sat in chairs of the zodiac, under a ceiling of a pale blue sky, appropriately dotted with fleecy clouds, and indeed most prettily painted. Flammarion is nothing if not astronomical. His whole apartment, which is itself au cinquieme, blossoms with such decoration.

"At the dinner I made the acquaintance of Miss Klumpke of the Paris Observatory, who has just translated my last article for the Bulletin of the Société Astronomique."

In fact before he left Paris for Africa he gave a talk to that society, on his observations of Mars. At Marseilles, meeting his old friend, Ralph Curtis, they crossed to Algiers and made excursions to Boghari and Biskra to test the atmosphere on the border of the Sahara. Not finding this satisfactory, he organized a small private caravan of his own for a journey of a few days into the desert, taking the telescope—doubtless the faithful six-inch—on a mule. His going off by himself across country seems to have worried his companions for fear he would lose his way; but he always turned up in the afternoon, and in time to observe when the stars came out. Curiously enough, he found that although the air was very clear they twinkled badly, so that while the atmosphere was transparent it was distinctly unsteady, for his purpose a very grave defect which excluded North Africa from the possible sites for his observatory. Satisfied on this point, he left Algiers in February.

From Marseilles he took the opportunity to visit Schiaparelli, to whom he owed so much of the incentive to study Mars, and found him at his observatory in Brera near Milan. With him he compared observations, much to his own satisfaction. The veteran looked middle-aged, but did not expect to make more discoveries, and said that at the preceding opposition the weather had been so bad that he saw almost nothing. So his mantle had definitely fallen on Percival when he began his observations at Flagstaff the year before.

Leaving Milan he started to visit Leo Brenner, who was also interested in Mars, and had his observatory at Lussinpiccolo, a rather inaccessible spot on the eastern coast of the Adriatic. In getting there he was much delayed by a heavy storm, and beguiled the time by working out a mathematical theory of the tides. Finally, he decided to go by rail to Pola, and thence by boat to Lussinpiccolo, where Brenner met him, insisting that he should stay with them. They proved most hospitable and kind, but he was not favorably impressed by the observatory or its work; and after a stay of a few days he returned through Cannes, Paris and London, sailing for America on March 19th, to land in New York on the 28th.

Meanwhile, the work on the lens and its apparatus had been finished; but it could not be set up until he was there, and arriving at the end of March there was no time to spare. For although the opposition of Mars did not occur until December 10th the planets would then be far past their nearest point, and there was much to see months before. In fact he, with Clark, arrived at Flagstaff shortly after the middle of July, and proceeded at once to put the glass into the telescope—no small difficulty, for the tube was so tight a fit in the dome which had housed the Brashear telescope that the lens had to be hoisted up and let into it through the shutter opening,—"quite a job," as he wrote, "for so delicate and yet heavy a thing as a 24-inch lens." However, it was successfully done, and the next morning at half past two observing began, and thereafter the dome knew no rest.[1]

In the letter last quoted he says that he has "taken a brand new house, finished indeed after I arrived, a little gem of a thing." Before long he had three houses on the hill there, and began that succession of charming hospitalities ending only with his life. Friends like Professor and Mrs. Barrett Wendell and Professor Charles S. Sargent visited there, while Professor Edward S. Morse and George R. Agassiz, who were interested in his investigations, paid him long visits; and since Flagstaff was on the direct road to Southern California, a paradise becoming more and more fashionable, many others stopped off on the way to see him and his observatory, whom he was always delighted to entertain, for he had an unusual capacity for doing so without interrupting the course of his work. Then there were excursions to the cave dwellings, the petrified forest, and other places of interest in the neighborhood, for he loved the country about him, and took pleasure in showing it to others. Sometimes these trips were unusual. "We all rode," he writes to a friend, "twelve miles out into the forest on the cow-catcher of a logging train, visited there a hole in the ground containing, if you crawl down through the chinks in the rocks several hundred feet, a

[1] Thereafter the equipment of the Observatory was steadily enlarged—notably by a 42-inch reflector in 1909—until now there are five domes, and much auxiliary apparatus.

thing we were not accoutered to do, real ice in midsummer; came back on the cow-catcher; and immensely enjoyed the jaunt. The acmes of excitement were the meeting of cattle on the track who showed much more unconcern of us than we of them. Indeed it was usually necessary for the fireman to get down and shoo them off. . . . Nevertheless we saw a real bull fight in a pretty little valley far from men where Greek met Greek for the possession of the herd. The two champions toed the line with great effect." Nor did his interest in literature abate, for a few weeks later he wrote to the same correspondent: "Send me, an' you love me, the best Chaucer at my expense."

Meanwhile the observations of Mars and the other planets went on with success, and he was naturally gratified when his telescope revealed something that others had failed to find, such as Professor "See's detection of the companion to Sirius which astronomers have been looking for in vain since its immersion some years ago in the rays of its primary due to its place in its orbit. The Lick hunted for it unsuccessfully last year"; the last remark being pointed by the fact that this rival had again been casting doubt upon his discoveries on Mars.

He observed without a break all summer and autumn, but aware that the atmosphere at Flagstaff was not so good in the winter, he decided to try that of Mexico, and thither he went in December taking the 24-inch telescope. Before the dome therefor was built he saw well with the six-inch; but for the larger glass the results were on the whole disappointing. Yet the observations in Mexico were by no means unproductive. To his father he writes: "In addition to all that I have told you before, Mr. Douglass has just made some in-

teresting studies of Jupiter's satellites, seeing them even better than we did at Flagstaff, and detecting markings on them
so well that they promise to give the rotation periods and so
lead to another pregnant chapter in tidal evolution." And
in another letter to him: "Mercury, Venus, Mars, and Jupiter's satellites have all revealed new things about themselves.
I intend to embody all of these things some day in a series of
volumes on the planets." Meanwhile, as during the observations of two years before, he was sending papers to various
scientific journals, American and foreign, about results obtained on Mars, Mercury and Venus; and about this time
Sir Robert Hart asked through Professor Headland permission to translate "Mars" into Chinese. One may add that the
first volume of the "Annals of the Lowell Observatory"
appeared that year (1897), the next in 1900.

CHAPTER XII

ILLNESS AND ECLIPSE

But his personal hopes of contributing further to science, or diffusing the knowledge learned, were destined to be sadly postponed. In the spring he left Mexico, and the telescope was returned to Flagstaff in May; but although he could stand observing day and night without sufficient sleep while stimulated by the quest, the long strain proved too much, and he came back to Boston nervously shattered. Such a condition is not infrequent with scholars who work at high speed, and although the diagnosis is simple the treatment is uncertain. The physicians put him to bed for a month in his father's house in Brookline, a measure that he always thought a mistake, believing that he would not have collapsed so completely under a different regimen. The progress everyone knows who has seen it, a very slow regaining of strength, with ups and downs, and after much discouragement—in his case about three years—a return to normal health.

After the doctors let him up from bed he sought rest in divers places, but the progress was slow and uneven, as it must be in such cases. Naturally letters at this period are few, short and far between. Only two, written to his father, appear to have been preserved, one from Bermuda, January 22, 1898:

"Dear Father:

I enclose what I think you will like to see, a copy made for you of a letter just received. *Festina lente* is nature's motto for me, and I try to make *nulla vestigia retrorsum*.

Affectionately your son
Percival

The copy enclosed is evidently of the letter from Professor Headland conveying Sir Robert Hart's request to translate "Mars" into Chinese. The other letter is on January 17, 1899, with no place—date, and it says: "Was much better; now can't sleep well. So it wags."

A year later, although not yet recovered, he was so much improved as to plan with Professor Todd of Amherst an expedition to Tripoli to observe a total eclipse of the sun. They took a 24-inch lens, from the observatory at Amherst, with a very light tube for transportation in four joints that would slip inside one another, and a device for photographing the solar corona; the lens of the telescope being the largest yet used in such an expedition. Sending the apparatus by freight, they themselves sailed on the German Steamship *St. Paul* from New York on January 17, 1900. He had regained his humor, if nothing else, for he heads his private journal of this exploit: "An Eclipse trip to Tripoli being the sequel to The Valet and the Valetudinarian"— not that he ever wrote anything under this last title, but it was a reference to what he had been through in the preceding two and a half years—and after inserting two flamboyant newspaper clippings, for which he was not responsible, he writes: "Further notices there were of which no notice need be taken; literary and professional murders all, of various degrees of atrocity."

After a few days in London, where he exchanged comments on the spectrum of Mars with Sir William Huggins, he passed on to Paris, and then Marseilles and Costabella where his widowed sister, Katharine Roosevelt, was staying. The eclipse was not to occur until the end of May, but there was much to be done in setting up the instruments, at which he was not needed; so as he saw his sister off for Italy he also bade good-bye for a time to Professor Todd, who left him to look up the telescopic apparatus and get it in place at Tripoli, while he stayed to recuperate for three months on the Riviera.

Here he found William James who, with his wife, was on a like quest to recruit from a similar case of neurasthenia, and at the same time to prepare his Gifford lectures. To his father Percival wrote on April 7: "Professor William James is living here now and we see each other all the time. He is pleased at having just been elected a corresponding member of the Academy of Sciences of Berlin, more for his children's sake than his own. This when he thought he should never be able to work again, and he wanted them to feel that their father had done something. Now, however, he is stronger and polishes off some Gifford lectures daily, a bit of it." They saw much of each other, being highly sympathetic physically and intellectually. Like himself, James had recovered, or not lost, his sense of humor, and quoted a remark he had heard "that ethics was a tardy consolation for the sins one had neglected to commit." And Percival was impressed by his saying that he "considered Darwin's greatness due to his great detail as increasing the probabilities; showing again how mere detail, mere bulk impresses, though probability be not furthered a bit." The last part of the sentence may be Percival's own conclusion rather than that of James, but it had clearly a bearing on his own minute study of the phenomena of Mars.

On the Riviera he made a number of pleasant acquaintances and he was well enough to enjoy seeing people; but, although he was writing a memoir for the American Academy on Venus, he was not yet up to really hard work. After trying in vain to think out mechanical explanations for the small ellipticity in the orbits of the planetary satellites he gave it up, and noted: "I actually am taking pleasure in chronicling this small beer (his solitary walks); pure thought proves so thorny to press." On April 3d he writes to his father: "I am trying to catch up with you and grandfather *Sed longo intervallo* so as to solace my solitary walks with fixed acquaintances." Both of these forebears had been interested in botany. In fact he walked much alone, studying the trees, shrubs and insects, and he writes: "I can converse with plants because they don't talk back, nor demand attention but accept it."

The time for the eclipse was drawing near, so after going to Florence to spend a few days more with his sister, he sailed from Genoa on May 16; trans-shipped at Naples, and going ashore in Sicily and Malta while the steamer was in port, reached Tripoli on May 24th. Travelling to out-of-the-way places in the Mediterranean was not a rapid process, and Tripoli then belonged to Turkey; but he found everything prepared by Professor Todd in the grounds of the American Consulate, and, fortunately, when the eclipse occurred four days later the sky was clear and everything went well. He was amused by the comments of the ignorant. "The Arabs," he wrote in his private journal, "the common folk, told their friends (beforehand) that the Christians lied, and when the affair came off, that they had no business to know being infidel." But he was as always interested in their ways and habits, mousing about the town with our consul and others, learning about the Turkish troops, and the Tuaureg camel drivers, inspecting a bakery, a macaroni factory, threshing and the weekly fair.

On June 3rd they sailed by an Italian steamer for Malta, but he left it at Tunis to go to the ruins of Carthage, which impressed him greatly; catching the boat again at Biserta, and at Malta trans-shipping again for Marseilles, he made his way to Paris. There the exhibition was open, and among other things he found his exhibit from Flagstaff, "poor waif, in a corner of the Palais de l'Optique and in another place stood confronted by four of my own drawings of Mars, un-labelled, unsubscribed. Felt badly for the poor orphans." He did not stay long, but went to England, and after spending a few days at the country house of some friends he had made on the Riviera, he sailed for home on July 4th. Shortly before leaving he had received telegrams telling of his father's un-expected death under an operation, cutting another link with his earlier life.

As yet not well enough to resume his work, he hired a farm house at Chocorua, and settled there on August 3rd for the rest of the summer. He enjoyed seeing the friends and neighbors who spent their vacations there; but, like some other men of science incapacitated by illness, he turned his attention to a field other than his own. As on the Riviera, this was flowers, butterflies, and especially trees; but he studied them more systematically, and with fuller notes. In October he gives a list, covering more than three pages, of the trees and shrubs in the woods, fields and swamps about

him in the order of their abundance. This interest he kept
up in later years at Flagstaff, corresponding with Professor
Charles S. Sargent, the Director of the Arnold Arboretum,
and sending him specimens of rare or unknown varieties,
some of which were named after him. So highly, indeed, did
Sargent rate him that after Percival's death he wrote a
memoir of him in *Rhodora*,[1] which it is well to transcribe in
full:

"That Percival Lowell took an active interest in trees was
probably not known to many persons, for he published only one
botanical paper and he had no botanical associates except in this
Arboretum. It is not surprising that a man with his active and
inquiring mind brought up in New England should, when he
found himself in Arizona, want to know something of the strange
plants which grew everywhere about him and which were so entirely unlike the plants which he had known as a boy in Massachusetts, and later in Japan and Korea. The love of plants, too,
was in his blood and only needed the opportunity of this new
field to make itself felt.

"Percival Lowell's great great grandfather, John Lowell, was
one of the original members of the Massachusetts Society for Promoting Agriculture and its second President, serving from 1796
until his death in 1802. He is less well known for his connection
with rural affairs than his son John Lowell, spoken of generally
in his day as "the Norfolk Farmer," and a generous and successful
promoter of scientific agriculture and horticulture in Massachusetts, whom Daniel Webster called "the uniform friend of all
sorts of rural economy." The second John Lowell became a member of the Agricultural Society in 1816 and served from the time
of his election until 1830 as its Corresponding Secretary, and as
one of the editors of its publication, *The Massachusetts Agricultural Repository and Journal*. During these years articles by him
on agriculture, horticulture and forestry are found in almost every

[1] Vol. 19, No. 218.

number. In volume v. published in 1819 there is an important paper by John Lowell on "The Gradual Diminution of the Forests of Massachusetts, and the importance of early attention to some effectual remedy, with extracts from the work of M. Michaux on the Forest Trees of North America." Volume vii. contains articles from his pen on "Some slight notice of the Larch tree (*Pinus Larix*), known in various parts of the country under the several names of Juniper, Hackmatack, and Larch"; on "Fruit Trees," signed by the Norfolk Gardener, and on "Raising the Oak from the Acorn and the best way of doing it." The last volume of this publication which appeared in 1832, when he was seventy-one years old, contains an article by John Lowell on "The Extraordinary Destruction of the last Year's Wood in Forest Trees and the probable Causes of it"; and on "Live Hedges for New England." The second John Lowell was active in establishing and maintaining the Botanic Garden of Harvard College and was one of the original members of the Massachusetts Horticultural Society. To the first annual festival of the Horticultural Society held in the Exchange Coffee House on State Street, September 19, 1829, he sent from his greenhouses in Roxbury Orange-trees covered with flowers and fruit and a bunch of grapes weighing three pounds.

"John Amory Lowell, the son of the second John Lowell and the grandfather of Percival Lowell, was deeply interested in botany and in 1845, thirty years after his graduation from Harvard College, began the collection of an herbarium and botanical library with the purpose of devoting himself seriously to the study of plants. He had made valuable collections and a large botanical library when the financial troubles of 1857 forced him to abandon botany and devote himself again to business affairs. His most valuable books were given by him to his friend Asa Gray and now form an important part of the library of the Gray Herbarium. His herbarium and his other botanical books were given to the Boston Society of Natural History. John Amory Lowell, like his father and grandfather, was a member of the Massachusetts Society for Promoting Agriculture. He was succeeded by his son John Lowell, who in turn was succeeded by his son, another

John Lowell, who of the fifth generation in direct descent from its second president is now a Trustee of this Society.

"Percival Lowell's love of plants certainly came to him naturally. I first met him in the Arboretum many years ago examining the collection of Asiatic Viburnums in which he was interested at that time, but it was not until 1910 that he began to send specimens to the Arboretum, including that of an Oak which he had found growing near his observatory and which so far as it is possible to judge is an undescribed species. Interest in this Oak led him to look for other individuals and to extend his botanical explorations. During these he visited Oak Creek Canyon, a deep cut with precipitous sides in the Colorado plateau which heads about twenty miles south of Flagstaff and carries in its bottom a small stream which finally finds its way into the Verde northwest and not far from Camp Verde. Lowell appears to have been the first botanist who visited the upper part, at least, of this canyon where he found a number of interesting plants, notably *Platanus Wrightii* and *Quercus arizonica,* which before his explorations were not known to extend into the United States from Mexico beyond the canyons of the mountain ranges of southern Arizona and New Mexico. In Oak Creek Canyon Lowell found a new Ash-tree somewhat intermediate between *Fraxinus quadrangulata* of the east and *F. anomala* of our southwestern deserts which will bear his name. Later Lowell explored Sycamore Canyon which is west of Oak Creek Canyon and larger and deeper than Oak Creek Canyon and, like it, cuts through the Colorado plateau and finally reaches the Verde near the mouth of Oak Creek.

"Juniperus in several species abound on the Colorado plateau, and Lowell became deeply interested in these trees and was preparing to write a monograph of our southwestern species. His observations on the characters and altitudinal range of the different species, illustrated by abundant material, have been of great service to me.

"Lowell's only botanical paper, published in the May and June issues of the *Bulletin of the American Geographic Society* in 1909, is entitled "The Plateau of the San Francisco Peaks in its Effect

on Tree Life." In this paper, which is illustrated by photographs
made by the author of all the important trees of the region, he
discusses the altitudinal distribution of these trees, dividing his
region into five zones which he illustrates by a number of charts
showing the distribution of vegetation in each. It contains, too,
an important and interesting discussion of the influence on temperature and therefore on tree growth of the larger body of earth
in a plateau as compared with a mountain peak where, on account of greater exposure, the earth cools more rapidly.[2]

"A bundle of cuttings of what is probably a new species of
Willow, to obtain which Lowell had made a long and hard
journey, with his last letter and a photograph of the Willow,
came only a few days before the telegram announcing his death.
Botany therefore occupied his thoughts during his last days on
earth.

"The death of Percival Lowell is a severe loss to the Arboretum.
He understood its purpose and sympathized with its efforts to
increase knowledge. Few collectors of plants have shown greater
enthusiasm or more imagination, and living as he did in what he
has himself described as "one of the most interesting regions of
the globe" there is every reason to believe that as a botanist
Percival Lowell would have become famous."

[2] Percival's statement of this may be found also in "Mars as the Abode of
Life," Chapter III.

CHAPTER XIII

MARS AND ITS CANALS

By the early spring of 1901 Percival was well over his illness, and fit to return to the Observatory for the oppositions of Mars in that year, in 1903 and in 1905. Shortly after he came back the services of Mr. Douglass came to an end, and he was fortunate in obtaining Dr. V. M. Slipher in 1901 and Mr. C. O. Lampland in the following year—two young men who were not only invaluable assistants to him, but during his lifetime, and ever since, have made distinguished contributions to science. Observing at all hours of the night was exacting work; and to anyone less enthusiastic, who did not see through the detail to its object, it might have been monotonous and wearisome. As he wrote himself, "Patient plodding is the road to results in science, and the shortest road in the end. Each year out here has seemed to me the best, which merely means that I hope I learn a little and that there is a vast deal to learn." He felt strongly the need of diligence and strict impartiality in ascertaining the facts, and distinguished it sharply from the imagination to be used in interpreting them. In describing his delineation of the canals he says, "Each drawing, it should be remembered, was as nearly an instantaneous picture of the disk as possible. It covered only a few minutes of observation, and was made practically as if the observer had never seen the planet before. In other words, the man was sunk in the

manner. Such mental effacement is as vital to good observation as mental assertion is afterward to pregnant reasoning. For a man should be a machine in collecting his
data, a mind in coördinating them. To reverse the process,
as is sometimes done, is not conducive to science." But
through all the exacting labor of the search he felt keenly
the joy of discovery, comparing himself to the explorers of
the Earth, and in the first chapter of "Mars and its Canals"
he tells us of the pleasure of a winter night spent in the Observatory.

The oppositions in 1901, 1903 and 1905 were not so favorable as those of 1894 and 1906–1907, because Mars was not so
near the Earth; the eccentricities in the orbits of the two
planets causing them to pass each other when Mars was far
from the Sun and therefore from the Earth whose eccentricity is less. Yet they had an advantage in the fact that,
unlike the earlier occasions, the south pole was tipped away
from the Earth, and the north pole was toward it, thus giving a good view of the northern polar cap, sub-arctic and
higher temperate zones, which had not been visible before.
Thus the seasonal changes could be observed in the opposite
hemisphere,—not an inconsiderable gain, because the dark
and light areas, that is, the natural vegetation and the deserts,
are not equally distributed over the planet, for the dark ones
occupy a much larger part of the southern, and the deserts
of the northern, hemisphere. Moreover, the use of a larger
lens and better atmosphere had shown that observations
could be carried on profitably for a longer period before and
after the actual opposition; until in 1905 it was possible to
cover what had been left unobserved of the Martian year
in the northern half of Mars.

No sooner was the third of these oppositions past than he wrote another book on the subject, with the title "Mars and its Canals"; and this in no sense a supplement to the earlier one, but an entirely new and independent presentation of the subject, covering the old ground and much more. He was enabled to do this because the copyright of the earlier work belonged to him. The later one was published by The Macmillan Company in December 1906, and dedicated to Schiaparelli. Like the earlier book, he wrote it by no means for astronomers alone, but for the interested public; and in the preface he tells why he did so: "To set forth science in a popular, that is in a generally understandable, form is as obligatory as to present it in a more technical manner. If men are to benefit by it, it must be expressed to their comprehension. To do this should be feasible for him who is master of his subject, and is both the best test of, and the best training to that post. . . . Nor is it so hard to make any well-grasped matter comprehensible to a man of good general intelligence as is commonly supposed. The whole object of science is to synthesize, and so simplify; and did we but know the uttermost of a subject we could make it singularly clear." At the same time there was nothing in these writings of the nature of what is commonly called popularizing science. He expounded his subject in a strictly scientific way, but avoided unfamiliar technical terms if possible, and sought to raise his readers or audience to his level of thought, not to descend to theirs. Such statements for the public were very often preceded by technical ones in the Bulletins of the Observatory or elsewhere, and yet it cannot be doubted that the former tended to alienate some scientific scholars who were slow to admit his discoveries, and did not sympathize with his method of presenting them, or perhaps with the attractive style of the man of letters as well as of exact thought.

Still there are pitfalls in taking the public into one's confidence; as he found in December 1900, when a telegram sent by the usual channels to the astronomical world, that the night before a projection had been observed on Mars that lasted seventy minutes, was taken by the press to mean an attempt by Martians to signal to the Earth, and as such was proclaimed all over America and Europe. The cause of the excitement, as he explained a year later to the American Philosophical Society in Philadelphia, was the reflection from a cloud on the horizon of the planet.

"Mars and its Canals" is frankly a demonstration that the planet is habitable, and that from what takes place there it must in fact be inhabited by highly intelligent beings. For that purpose the book is divided into four parts, entitled: Natural Features; Non-Natural (that is, artificial) Features; The Canals in Action; and Explanation. His general thesis, which he was to expound more fully later (and which although not essential to his argument for life on Mars he connected therewith) was that all planets go through the same process of development—varying, however, with their size which determines their power to retain the gases of their atmosphere—and that one element therein is the gradual leakage of water through cracks into its interior as the planet cools. He cites geologists to prove that the oceans formerly covered much more of the surface of the Earth than they do now; argues that the desert belts around it are of comparatively recent geologic origin, as shown by the petrified forest of Arizona; and points out the

similarity in color, as seen from the San Francisco Peaks, of
the forested hills and the painted desert there, to that of the
blue-green and reddish-ochre spaces of Mars as presented by
the telescope. He notes also that to get water in our deserts
plants and animals have sought the higher altitudes, and are
able to exist and multiply in an air less dense and a climate
cooler with a shorter warm season than in their natural
habitat, adjusting themselves to these conditions.

This idea of the lack of water on Mars he derives from
observation of its surface and the changes thereon; for the
supply of water is in great part locked up in the snow or ice
of the polar caps during the Martian winters of the two
hemispheres and distributed over its surface as summer
comes on. Therefore he naturally begins his account of the
natural features of the planet by a description of these polar
snow caps, their formation and melting. In doing so he
cannot resist a sarcastic reference to the endless enthusiasm,
useless expenditure of money and labor, and the scientific
futility of arctic exploration.

"Polar expeditions exert an extreme attraction on certain
minds, perhaps because they combine the maximum of
hardship with the minimum of headway. Inconclusiveness
certainly enables them to be constantly renewed, without
loss either of purpose or prestige. The fact that the pole has
never been trod by man constitutes the lodestone to such
undertakings; and that it continues to defy him only whets
his endeavor the more. Except for the demonstration of the
polar drift-current conceived of and then verified by Nansen,
very little has been added by them to our knowledge of the
globe. Nor is there specific reason to suppose that what they
might add would be particularly vital. Nothing out of the

way is suspected of the pole beyond the simple fact of being so positioned. Yet for their patent inconclusion they continue to be sent in sublime superiority to failure.

"Martian polar expeditions, as undertaken by the astronomers, are the antipodes of these pleasingly perilous excursions in three important regards, which if less appealing to the gallery commend themselves to the philosopher. They involve comparatively little hardship; they have accomplished what they set out to do; and the knowledge they have gleaned has proved fundamental to an understanding of the present physical condition of the planet."

Then follows the story of the melting of the polar snows, the darkening of the blue-green areas by the growth of vegetation due to the flow of water; and a summary, at the close of Part I (Natural Features), of the reasons for believing that from its atmosphere, temperature, and the actual, though scanty, supply of water, Mars is capable of supporting life. In fact the presence of vegetation proves that life of that kind does exist, in spite of the fact that five-eighths of the surface is desert; and if plants can live animals might also. But, unlike vegetation, they could not be readily seen, and save in the case of intelligent operation on a large scale, their presence could not be detected. This is the significance of the canals, to which much of the observation of the last three oppositions was directed.

Close to the limit of vision, and only to be seen at moments when the atmosphere is steady, the fainter canals are very hard to observe. Percival describes the experience in this way:

"When a fairly acute eyed observer sets himself to scan the telescopic disk of the planet in steady air, he will, after noting the dazzling contour of the white polar cap and the sharp outlines of the blue-green areas, of a sudden be made aware of a vision as of a thread stretched somewhere from the blue-green across the orange areas of the disk. Gone as quickly as it came, he will instinctively doubt his own eyesight, and credit to illusion what can so unaccountably disappear. Gaze as hard as he will, no power of his can recall it, when, with the same startling abruptness, the thing stands before his eyes again. Convinced, after three or four such showings, that the vision is real, he will still be left wondering what and where it was. For so short and sudden are its apparitions that the locating of it is dubiously hard. It is gone each time before he has got its bearings.

"By persistent watch, however, for the best instants of definition, backed by the knowledge of what he is to see, he will find its coming more frequent, more certain and more detailed. At last some particularly propitious moment will disclose its relation to well known points and its position be assured. First one such thread and then another will make its presence evident; and then he will note that each always appears in place. Repetition *in situ* will convince him that these strange visitants are as real as the main markings, and are as permanent as they."

Strangely enough fine lines, from the continuity of the impression they make upon the eye, can be recognized when of a thickness that would be invisible in the case of a mere dot. To determine how narrow a line on Mars would be perceptible, experiments were made with a wire of a certain size, noting the limit of distance at which it could be seen; and then, from the magnifying power of the telescope, it was found that a Martian canal would be visible down to about a mile wide. From this the conclusion was drawn that the canals probably ran from two or three up to fifteen or twenty miles in width, the minimum being much less than had been thought at earlier oppositions. The distance apart of the two branches of double canals he estimated at about seventy-five to one hundred and eighty miles, save in one case where, if a true instance of doubling, it is over four hundred. Of the oases, whereof one hundred and eighty-six had been observed, much the larger part were from seventy-five to one hundred miles in diameter.

The later oppositions enabled him also to complete the topography of the planet, showing that the canals were a vast system, running from the borders of both polar caps, through the dark areas of natural vegetation where they connected, at obviously convenient points, with a still more complex network in the ochre, or desert, regions, and thus across the equator into the corresponding system in the other hemisphere. By this network the greater part of the canals could receive water alternately from the melting of the north and south polar caps, or twice yearly, the Martian year, however, being almost twice as long as our own. But to perfect his proof that this actually takes place he had to show that the canals, that is the streaks of vegetation bordering waterways, sprang into life—thereby becoming visible or darker—in succession as the water spread from the poles to the tropics; and this he did with his usual thoroughness at the opposition of 1903.

Since there was then no mechanical means of measuring the variations in visibility of the canals,—and under the atmospheric conditions at any place in the world perhaps there never will be,—the record had to be made by the eye, that is in drawings by the observer as he saw the canals; and these, as he said, must be numerous, consecutive and extended in time. The consecutive could not be perfectly carried out because "as Mars takes about forty minutes longer to turn than the Earth, such confronting (of the observer) occurs later and later each night by about forty minutes, until finally it does not occur at all while Mars is suitably above the horizon; then the feature passes from sight to remain hidden till the difference of the rotations brings it round into view again. There are thus times when a given region is visible, times when it is not, and these succeed each other in from five to six weeks, and are called presentations. For about a fortnight at each presentation a region is centrally enough placed to be well seen; for the rest of the period either ill-placed or on the other side of the planet." But with changes as gradual and continuous as those of the darkening of the canals this did not prove a serious drawback to the continuity of the record.

There was another element in the problem. The drawing being the estimate of the observer on the comparative darkness of the markings from time to time it was of the greatest importance to avoid any variation in personal estimates, and therefore Percival made all the drawings himself. From April 6 to May 26 he drew the planet every twenty-four hours, and although "the rest of the time did not equal this perfection, no great gap occurred, and one hundred and forty-three nights were utilized in all. . . . But even this does not give an idea of the mass of the data. For by the method employed about 100 drawings were used in the case of each canal, and as 109 canals were examined this gave 10,900 separate determinations upon which the ultimate result depended."

For each canal he plotted the curve of its diminishing or increasing visibility as the season advanced, and this curve he called the cartouche of the canal. Now combining the cartouches of all the canals in each zone of latitude, he found that those in the several zones began to become more distinct—that is the vegetation began to come to life—in a regular and approximately uniform succession, taking from the northern arctic down to the equator and past it to the southern sub-tropic about eighty Martian days. From north latitude 72° to the equator, a distance of 2,650 miles, took fifty-two of these days, at a speed of fifty-one miles a day, or 2.1 miles an hour. Now all this is precisely the opposite of what happens on the Earth, where vegetation in the spring starts in the part of the temperate zone nearest to the equator, and as the season advances travels toward the pole; the reason for the difference being, he says, that what is needed on Earth to make the sap run is the warmth of the sun, what is needed on Mars is water that comes from the melting of the polar snows. He points out also that the water cannot flow through the canals by nature, because on the surface of a planet in equilibrium gravity would not draw it in any direction toward or away from the equator. "No natural force propels it, and the inference is forthright and inevitable that it is artificially helped to its end. There seems to be no escape from this deduction." In short, since water certainly cannot flow by gravity both ways in the same canal, the inhabitants of Mars have not only dug the canals, but pump the water through them.

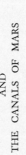

OBSERVING AND DRAWING

THE CANALS OF MARS

In recapitulating the reasons for the artificial character of the canals he shows a most natural annoyance with people who doubted the validity of his observations; and, in dealing with the evidence to be drawn from the fact that they run on great circles, that is on the shortest lines from one point to another, he writes: "For it is the geodetic precision which the lines exhibit that instantly stamps them to consciousness as artificial. The inference is so forthright as to be shared by those who have not seen them to the extent of instant denial of their objectivity. Drawings of them look too strange to be true. So scepticism imputes to the draftsman their artificial fashioning, not realizing that by so doing it bears unconscious witness to their character. For in order to disprove the deduction it is driven to deny the fact. Now the fact can look after itself and will be recognized in time."

This last prophecy was largely verified before these three oppositions of the planet came to an end. In 1901 photography was tried without success so far as the canals were concerned. For the stars it had worked very well, for to quote again: "Far less sensitive than the retina the dry plate has one advantage over its rival,—its action is cumulative. The eye sees all it can in the twentieth of a second; after that its perception, instead of increasing, is dulled, and no amount of application will result in adding more. With the dry plate it is the reverse. Time works for, not against it. Within limits, themselves long, light affects it throughout the period it stands exposed and, roughly speaking, in direct ratio to the time elapsed. Thus the camera is able to record stars no human eye has ever caught and to register the structure of nebulae the eye tries to resolve in vain.

"Where illumination alone is concerned the camera reigns

supreme; not so when it comes to a question of definition. Then by its speed and agility the eye steps into its place, for the atmosphere is not the void it could be wished, through which the light-waves shoot at will. Pulsing athwart it are air-waves of condensation and rarefaction that now obstruct, now further, the passage of the ray. By the nimbleness of its action the eye cunningly contrives to catch the good moments among the poor and carry their message to the brain. The dry plate by its slowness is impotent to follow. To register anything it must take the bad with the better to a complete confusion of detail. For the air-waves throw the image first to one place and then to another, to a blotting of both."

There lay the difficulty which Mr. Lampland, then new to the Observatory, took up in 1903. The photographs, though better, still did not show the canals. Various adjustments were then made with the telescope; all manner of plates were tried between the rapid and the well-defining ones; and finally in 1905 upon the plates canals appeared, thirty-eight in all and one of them double.[1] On learning of the success Schiaparelli wrote in wonder to Percival, "I should never have believed it possible"; and the British Royal Photographic Society awarded its medal to Mr. Lampland.

With the observations of 1905 ended until the next opposition of the planet an exploration and a romance of which he wrote:

"To some people it may seem that the very strangeness of Martian life precludes for it an appeal to human interest. To me this is but a near-sighted view. The less the life there proves a counterpart of our earthly state of things, the more

[1] Their existence was proved, although the grain of the best plates is too coarse to distinguish between sharp lines and diffuse bands.

it fires fancy and piques inquiry as to what it be. We all have felt this impulse in our childhood as our ancestors did before us, when they conjured goblins and spirits from the vasty void, and if our energy continue we never cease to feel its force through life. We but exchange, as our years increase, the romance of fiction for the more thrilling romance of fact. As we grow older we demand reality, but so this requisite be fulfilled the stranger the realization the better we are pleased. Perhaps it is the more vivid imagination of youth that enables us all then to dispense with the hall-mark of actuality upon our cherished visions; perhaps a deeper sense of our own oneness with nature as we get on makes us insist upon getting the real thing. Whatever the reason be, certain it is that with the years a narration, no matter how enthralling, takes added hold of us for being true. But though we crave this solid foothold for our conceptions, we yield on that account no jot or tittle of our interest for the unexpected."

CHAPTER XIV

THE SOLAR SYSTEM

IN the intervals of personal observation Percival was often giving lectures or writing on astronomical subjects for the publications of the Observatory, and for scientific societies and periodicals. The substance of most of these found their way into his books, which are summations or expositions of his conclusions. In December 1902, for example, he gave six lectures on "The Solar System" at the Massachusetts Institute of Technology, of which he was a non-resident professor, and they were published by Houghton, Mifflin & Company. Then in the autumn of 1906 he gave a course of eight lectures at the Lowell Institute in Boston on "Mars as the Abode of Life." These were so crowded that they had to be repeated, were then printed as six papers in the *Century Magazine,* and finally re-published by The Macmillan Company under the same title. Two years later, in the winter of 1909, he gave at the Massachusetts Institute of Technology, another course of six lectures on "Cosmic Physics: The Evolution of Worlds," which were brought out in December by the same publisher with the latter half of the title. Although their names are so diverse, and far more is told of Mars in the book whose title contains its name, they all deal essentially with the same subject, the evolution of the planets and the development and end of life upon them. In the Preface to

"Mars as the Abode of Life,"—for a preface, although printed at the beginning, is always written after the book is finished, and is the author's last word to the reader, giving his latest thought as the work is being launched,—he tells us: [1] "Though dealing specifically with Mars, the theme of the lectures was that of planetary evolution in general, and this book is thus a presentation of something which Professor Lowell has long had in mind and of which his studies of Mars form but a part, the research into the genesis and development of what we call a world; not the mere aggregating of matter, but what that aggregation inevitably brings forth. The subject which links the Nebular Hypothesis to the Darwinian Theory, bridging the evolutionary gap between the two, he has called planetology, thus designating the history of the planet's individual career. It is in this light that Mars is here regarded: how it came to be what it is and how it came to differ from the Earth in the process."

At each opposition, in fact at every opposition during Percival's life and long thereafter, Mars was observed at Flagstaff and more detail was discovered confirming what had been found before. He tells of a slight change in the estimated tilt in its axis; the fact that the temperature is warmer than was earlier supposed; [2] and he had found how to discover the gases by spectroscopic analysis applied according to an ingenious device of his own known as "Velocity Shift" and much used thereafter. [3] He tells also of an

[1] While written in the third person the words are clearly his own.

[2] His determination of the Martian temperature has since been very closely verified.

[3] In a letter to Dr. V. M. Slipher on Oct. 4, 1902 he writes:

"There has come into my head a new way for detecting the spectral lines due to a planet's own atmospheric absorption, and I beg you will apply it to Mars so soon as the Moon shall be in position to make a comparison spectrum.

It is this. At quadrature of an exterior planet we are travelling toward that ingenious and elaborate experiment with wires, and with lines on a wooden disk, which showed that such lines can be perceived at a greater distance and therefore of smaller size than had been supposed, so that the canals might have less width than had been assumed. It is, however, needless, in describing his planetary theory, to do more than allude to his evidence of Martian habitation drawn from the canals, with which the reader is already familiar. Curiously enough, however, it is interesting to note that on September 9, 1909, about the time when "The Evolution of Worlds" was going to press, a strange phenomenon appeared in Mars. Two striking canals were seen where none had ever been seen before, and the most conspicuous on that part of the disk. Moreover, they were photographed. After examining all the maps of canals made at Flagstaff and elsewhere, Percival discussed them in the Observatory Bulletin No. 45, and concluded that they must not only be new to us, but new to Mars since its previous corresponding season of two of our years before: "something *extra ordinem naturae*." We may here leave Mars for the time, and turn to the more extensive study of the evolution of the planetary system.

The desire to rise from a particular case to a more general law was characteristic of his attitude of mind, constructive

---

planet at the rate of 18.5 miles a second and we are carrying of course our own atmosphere with us. Our motion shortens all the wave-lengths sent us from the planet, including those which have suffered absorption in *its* atmosphere. When the waves reach *our* atmosphere those with a suitable wave-length are absorbed by it and these wave-lengths are unaffected by our motion since it is at rest as regards us. Even were the two atmospheres alike the absorbed wave-lengths reaching us would thus be different since the one set, the planet's, have been shifted by our motion toward it while the other set, our own, are such as they would be at rest. We thus have a criterion for differentiating the two. And the difference should be perceptible in your photographs. For the shift of Jupiter's lines due to rotation is such as 8. $\times$ 2. $=$ 16 miles a second produces, which is less than 18.5 and about what you will get now."

and insatiable, and appears throughout these volumes. It may
have been influenced by his great master Benjamin Peirce,
who ever treated any mathematical formula as a special instance of a more comprehensive one. In such a subject as the
evolution of the planets, especially of life on them, it involved dipping into many sciences, beyond the physical laws
of matter; and he says in the same preface: "As in all theses,
the cogency of the conclusion hangs upon the validity of each
step in the argument. It is vital that each of these should be
based on all that we know of natural laws and the general
principles underlying them." This did not mean that all his
premises would be universally accepted, but that he found
out all he could about them, convincing himself of their accuracy and of the validity of the conclusions he draws therefrom. That is all any man of science can do in a subject
larger than his own special, and therefore limited, field.

But from the time of his resumption of research and the
direction of the observatory in 1901, he was constantly enlarging his own field by the study of astrophysical subjects,
and the methods for their determination. With this object he
was initiating and encouraging planetary photography. He
was constantly writing Dr. V. M. Slipher about procuring
and using spectrographic apparatus and about the results obtained by him therefrom. By this process the rotations of
planets were determined; and the spectra of the major ones
—often reproduced in astronomical works—have been a
puzzle to astrophysicists until their interpretation in very
recent years. He was interested also in nebulae, especially
in spiral ones, taking part in Dr. Slipher's pioneering spectrographic work at the observatory, which showed that they
were vast aggregations of stars of different spectral types,

moving with great speed, and far beyond the limits of our universe. For over fifteen years the observatory was almost alone in this field of research, as well as in that of globular clusters. It is in fact, the discovery of the rapid motion of the spiral nebulae away from the solar system that has given rise to the conception of an expanding universe.

But these discoveries were still largely in the future, and to return to his books on the planetary system it may be noted that in the two larger and more popular ones the general planetary theory is expounded in the text, while the demonstrations of the more complex statements made, and the mathematical calculations involved, are relegated to a mass of notes at the end of the volume.

The first of his books on the solar system is the small volume bearing that title; but since all three of the books here described are several expositions of the same subject it may be well to treat his views on each topic in connection with the work in which he deals with it most fully. Indeed, "The Solar System" is not a general treatise, but rather a discussion of some striking points, and it is these which one thinks of in connection therewith.

In considering the origin of the planets he had become much interested in the meteors, shooting stars, meteoric streams and comets, all or almost all of which he regarded as parts of the solar system, revolving about the Sun in elliptic orbits, often so eccentric as to appear parabolas.[4] The old idea that comets came from outer space and therefore travelled in hyperbolas can, he points out, be true of few, if any, of them. "Very few, three or four perhaps, hint at

[4] So far as the shooting stars are concerned this opinion was based upon their velocities, which have since been found in many cases to be greater than was then supposed.

hyperbolas. Not one is such beyond question." Many of them are associated with the meteoric streams with which everyone is familiar at certain seasons of the year. Indeed seventy-six of these associations were then known, and comets sometimes break up into such streams.

Now if the comets are travelling in orbits around the Sun they must be throughout their course within its control, and not within that of some other star; and therefore he computes how far the Sun's control extends. Taking for this purpose our nearest star, α Centauri, a double with a total mass twice that of the Sun, at a distance of 275,000 astronomical units, in other words that number of times our distance from the Sun, he finds that the point at which its attraction and that of the Sun become equal is 114,000 of these units. This he calls the extent of the Sun's domain, certainly an area large enough for any, or almost any, comet known.[5]

He then turns to some of the planets,—Mercury to show the effect of tidal action in slowing the rotation of a planet or satellite, and causing it to turn the same face always to its master.[6] This involved a highly interesting comparison of Newton's theory of the tides, long generally accepted, but not taking enough account of the planet's rotation, and that of Sir George Darwin based upon the effect of such rotation. The general conceptions are even more different than the results, and the later theory is less concerned with the tides in oceans, which probably affect only our Earth, than with those of a planet in a fluid or viscous condition, which may still continue to some extent after the surface has become

[5] Opic has recently shown that the sun's effective domain is even larger.
[6] Later observations seem to show that Mercury's periods of rotation and revolution are not the same, but nearly so.

partly solidified. He therefore studies the tide raising force, and the tendency to retardation of rotation, by the Sun on the planets, and by these on their satellites while still in a fluid state, tabulating some very striking results.

What he says about Mars is more fully dealt with in his other writings; and the same is true of Saturn's rings, except for the reference to the calculation by Edward Roche of the limit of possible approach by a fluid satellite to its planet without being disrupted, and for the fact that this limit in Saturn's case falls just beyond the outer edge of the rings. In discussing Saturn's satellites he brings out a curious analogy between the order of distribution of these attendants of the three best known major planets and the order of the planets themselves about the Sun. In each case the largest of the bodies so revolving is nearly in the centre of the line, as in the case of Jupiter among the planets; the second largest the next, or not far, beyond, as in the case of Saturn; while there is another maximum farther in, for as the Earth is larger than any planet on either side until Jupiter is reached, so a like order is found in the satellites of Jupiter, Saturn and Uranus. In other words, the size in each case rises with increasing distance, falls off, then rises again to the largest and thence declines. This he believed cannot be an accidental coincidence, but the result of a law of development as yet unexplained.

To the ordinary reader the most novel thing he says about Jupiter relates to its family of comets, for no less than thirty-two of these bodies have their aphelia, or greatest distance from the Sun, near its orbit. Moreover, their ascending nodes—that is the place where their paths if inclined to the plane of the ecliptic pass through it—are close to its orbit.

At some time, therefore, in the vast ages of the past they must have passed close to the planet, and if so have had their orbits greatly changed by its attraction. He considers the various effects Jupiter may have upon a comet, and shows —contrary to the opinion of Professor H. A. Newton— that any such body moving by the attraction of the Sun would be going too fast for Jupiter to capture completely. Then he takes up other effects of deflection. The comet's speed may be accelerated and its direction changed even so much as to drive it out of the solar system; it may be retarded so that its path is contracted and the aphelion drawn nearer to the planet's orbit. After calculating the possible conditions and analyzing the actual orbits of Jupiter's family, he comes to the provisional conclusion that these comets have been drawn from the neighborhood. "It is certain," he says, "that Jupiter has swept his neighborhood. . . . If we consider the comet aphelia of short-period comets, we shall notice that they are clustered about the path of Jupiter and the path of Saturn, thinning out to a neutral ground between, where there are none. Two-thirds of the way from Jupiter's orbit to Saturn's, space is clear of them, the centre of the gap falling at 8.4 astronomical units from the sun. . . .

"Jupiter is not the only planet that has a comet family. All the large planets have the like. Saturn has a family of two, Uranus also of two, Neptune of six; and the spaces between these planets are clear of comet aphelia; the gaps prove the action.

"Nor does the action, apparently, stop there. Plotting the aphelia of all the comets that have been observed, we find, as we go out from the Sun, clusters of them at first, representing, respectively, Jupiter's, Saturn's, Uranus', and Neptune's family;[7] but the clusters do not stop with Neptune. Beyond that planet is a gap, and then at 49 and 50 astronomical units we find two more aphelia, and then nothing again till we reach 75 units out.

"This can hardly be accident; and if not chance, it means a planet out there as yet unseen by man, but certain sometime to be detected and added to the others. Thus not only are comets a part of our system now recognized, but they act as finger-posts to planets not yet known."

We shall hear more of this last suggestion hereafter.

In both "Mars as the Abode of Life" and "The Evolution of Worlds," he accepts the proposition that our present solar system began with a collision with some dark body from interstellar space, as had been suggested by Chamberlin and Moulton a few years before. He points out that stars which have finished contracting, grown cold and ceased to be luminous, must exist, and although we cannot see them directly we know about some of them,—such as the dark companion of Algol, revolving around it and cutting off two-thirds of its light every three days. Many dark wanderers there must be, and the *novae,* as he says, are sometimes, at least, due to a collision with such a body,—not necessarily an actual impact, but an approach so near that the star is sprung asunder by the tidal effect. In such a case the opposite sides of the victim would be driven away from it, and if it was rotating would form spirals. Now we know that the apparently empty spaces in our solar system still contain a vast number of little meteoric particles, which as judged from their velocity do not fall from outer space,

[7] It now appears very improbable that these are real comet families.

but are members of our system travelling in their own orbits around the sun. As he puts it, "Could we rise a hundred miles above the Earth's surface we should be highly sorry we came, for we should incontinently be killed by flying brickbats. Instead of masses of a sunlike size we should have to do with bits of matter on the average smaller than ourselves [8] but hardly on that account innocuous, as they would strike us with fifteen hundred times the speed of an express train." That these meteorites are moving in the same direction as the Earth he shows by an ingenious calculation of the proportion that in such a case would be seen at sunrise and sunset, which accords with the observed facts. Moreover, their chemical composition shows that they were once parts of a great hot body from which they have been expelled.

The meteorites that are seen because they become hot and luminous in traversing our atmosphere, and occasionally fall upon the Earth, are the remnants of vastly larger numbers formerly circling about the sun, but which, by collision and attraction, were, as he describes, gathered into great masses, thus forming the planets. The force of gravity gradually compacted these fragments closer and closer together, thereby generating heat which if the body were homogeneous would be in proportion to the square of its mass. The larger the planet therefore the more heat it would generate, and owing to the fact that mass is in proportion to the cube and its radiating surface to the square of the diameter the slower it would radiate, and thus lose,

---

[8] Recent results indicate that these are much smaller, and sometimes move faster, than was formerly believed.

its heat, so that the larger ones would be hotter and remain hot longer than the smaller ones.

Some of the planets may once have been white-hot, and luminous of themselves, some were certainly red-hot, some only darkly warm; all growing cooler after the amount radiated exceeded the amount generated. Now by the difference in the heat generated and retained by the larger and smaller bodies he explains the diverse appearance of those whose surfaces we know, the Earth, Mars and the Moon. As the surface cools it forms a crust, but if the interior still remains molten it will continue to contract, the crust will be too large for it and crinkle, like the skin of a dried apple; and this will be more true of a large than a small body. "In like manner is volcanic action relatively increased, and volcanoes arise, violent and widespread, in proportion; since these are vents by which the molten matter under pressure within finds exit abroad." By a calculation, which agrees with the formula of Laplace, he finds that the effective internal heat of the Earth might be 10,000 degrees Fahrenheit, enough to account for all the phenomena; and for Mars only 2,000, which is below the melting point of iron, and would not cause volcanic action. Now the observations of Mars at Flagstaff show that there can be no mountains on it more than two or three thousand feet high, and that the surface is singularly flat.

But here he met a difficulty; for the Moon ought to be flatter still if it had evolved in the ordinary way, whereas it has enormous volcanic cones, craters 17,000 feet high, some exceeding 100 miles in diameter, and a range of mountains rising to nearly 30,000 feet. An explanation he finds in the analysis of the action of the tides in the Earth-Moon

system by Sir George Darwin, who showed that when traced
backward it "lands us at a time when the Moon might have
formed a part of the Earth's mass, the two rotating together
as a single pear-shaped body in about five hours. . . . For
in that event the internal heat which the Moon carried away
with it must have been that of the parent body—the amount
the Earth-Moon had been able to amass. Thus the Moon
was endowed from the start of its separate existence with
an amount of heat the falling together of its own mass could
never have generated. Thus its great craters and huge volcanic cones stand explained. It did not originate as a separate body, but had its birth in a rib of Earth." [9]

The Flagstaff site having been selected for the purpose of
planetary observation yielded facts less easily detected elsewhere. Mercury, for instance, is so near the Sun that it
could be observed in the dark only a short time after sunset and before sunrise, an obstacle that gave rise to errors
of fact. Schiaparelli led the way to better results by observing this planet in broad daylight. Up to that time it had
been supposed to rotate on its axis in about twenty-four
hours, and therefore to have a day and night like those of
the Earth, but daylight observation showed him markings
constant on its illuminated face, and therefore that it turns
nearly the same side to the Sun. Before knowing his conclusions, and therefore independently, the study of Mercury
was taken up at Flagstaff in 1896, and the result was a complete corroboration of his work. It showed that, as in the
case of the Moon with the Earth, tidal action on the still
partially fluid mass had slowed its rotation until it has little

[9] This theory, though generally held till 1930, has apparently been disproved
by Jeffries.

with regard to the central body around which it revolves. He discovered also other facts about Mercury, which Schiaparelli had not, that its size, mass and density had not been accurately measured.

A similar discovery about the period of rotation had been made in the case of Venus. For more than two centuries astronomers had felt sure that this period was just under twenty-four hours, figured, indeed, to the minute. But again it was Schiaparelli who doubted, and once more by observing the planet at noon; when he noted that the markings on the disk did not change from day to day, and concluded that the same side was always pointed at the Sun. At Flagstaff in 1896 his observations were verified and the inference later confirmed by the spectroscope, which was, indeed, first brought to the Observatory for that purpose. Thus Venus, which from its distance from the Sun, its size and density, is most like the Earth, turns out to be in a totally different condition, one face baked by unending glare, the other chilled in interstellar night, and as he puts it: "To Venus the Sun stands substantially stock-still in the sky,—. . . No day, no seasons, practically no year, diversifies existence or records the flight of time. Monotony eternalized,—such is Venus' lot." [10]

On the movements and physical condition of the Earth it was needless to dwell, and he passed to the asteroids. He describes how they began to be discovered at the beginning of the last century by searching for a planet that would fill a gap in Bode's law. This, a formula of arithmetical pro-

[10] The periods of revolution and rotation have since appeared not to be exactly the same.

gression for the distances of the planets from the Sun, has proved not to be a law at all, especially since the discovery of Neptune which is much nearer than the formula required; but for nearly a century it had a strong influence on astronomic thought, and the gap in the series between Mars and Jupiter was searched for the missing link. Two were found, then two more, about the middle of the last century another, and then many, smaller and smaller, until by the time Percival wrote six hundred were known, and their number seems limitless. Only the four first found, he remarks, exceed a hundred miles in diameter, the greater part being hardly over ten or twenty. But here he points out a notable fact, that they are not evenly distributed throughout this space; and although massed in a series growing thicker toward its centre there are many gaps, even close to the centre, where few or no asteroids are found. Now it is the large size and attraction of Jupiter by which Percival explains the presence of asteroids with gaps in their ranks, instead of a planet, in the space between it and Mars; but we shall hear much more of this subject when we come to his work on Saturn's rings and the order in the distribution of the planets.

Jupiter, he tells us, having a mass 318 times that of the Earth, and a volume 1400 times as large, is much less dense, not much more than water, in short still fluid; and as it has a tremendous spin, rotating in less than ten hours, it is more oblate than the Earth; that is, the diameter at its equator is larger in proportion to that from pole to pole. The observations at Flagstaff brought out some interesting facts: first, that the dark belts of cloud that surround it are red, looking as if the planet within were still molten; [11] second, that the bright central belt lies exactly upon its equator, without regard to, and hence independent of, its tilt toward the Sun, and that the belts of cloud on each side appear at the planet's morning just as they left it in the evening. All which shows that Jupiter's cloud formation is not due to the Sun, but to its own internal heat, an interpretation of the phenomena that has a direct bearing on his explanation of the Earth's carboniferous age.

Saturn is still less dense, even more oblate; but its most extraordinary feature is of course the rings. Assumed by the early astronomers to be solid and continuous, they were later shown to have concentric intervals, and to be composed of discrete particles. They have usually been supposed flat, but when the position of the planet was such that they were seen on edge knots or beads appeared upon them; and in 1907 these were studied critically at Flagstaff, when it was found that the shadows of the rings on the planet were not uniform, but had dark cores; these thicker places lying on the outer margin of each ring where it came to one of the intervals. These phenomena he explained in the same way as the distribution of the intervals among the asteroids.[12]

About Uranus and Neptune he tells us in this book little that was not known, and save for their orbits, masses and satellites not much was known of their condition. But later, in 1911, the spectroscope at Flagstaff determined the rotation period of Uranus, afterwards precisely duplicated at

[11] Radiometric measures of late years show the outer surface of Jupiter to be at a very low temperature.

[12] As these thickenings, which he called tores, were not perceived the next time the rings were seen edgewise—although probably there—it is needless to dwell more upon them.

the Lick; and later still the spectral bands in the vast atmosphere of the giant planets were identified as due to methane,
or marsh, gas.[13]

[13] By continued, and quite recent, study at Flagstaff the content of this gas
has been found to be for Jupiter and Saturn one half, for Uranus five times
and for Neptune twenty-five times the amount of the atmosphere of the Earth.

A reader who seeks to know more of the later theories of the Solar System
may find them in the book with that name by Russell, Dugan and Stewart.

CHAPTER XV

LATER EVOLUTION OF THE PLANETS

AFTER the planets had been formed through the aggregation of revolving fragments driven off by the catastrophic collision from the Sun, and after they had attained their maximum heat in the process, they began, he says, to go through six stages:

I. The Sun-Stage, when they were white-hot and gave out light. This could have been true only of the largest ones if any.

II. The Molten Stage, when they were still red-hot, but not enough to give light, in which are now the four great outer planets.

III. The Solidifying Stage, when a crust formed, and the surface features of the planet began to assume their character. Here the science of geology takes its start with the metamorphic rocks, and it is the dividing line between the inner, smaller, and the outer, larger, planets.

IV. The Terraqueous Stage, when the surface has become substantially stable, there are great oceans gradually diminishing in size, and land gradually increasing. This is the stage of the sedimentary rocks, the time when the planet passes from its own supply of heat to dependence upon that of the sun; the stage when life begins, and the one in which the Earth is now.

V. The Terrestrial Stage, when the oceans have disappeared, and water is scarce, the one in which Mars is now.

VI. The Dead Stage, where are already the Moon and the satellites of other planets.

On the question of the origin of life Percival took the mechanistic view: "Upon the fall of the temperature to the condensing point of water, occurred another event in the evolution of our planet, the Earth, and one of great import to us: life arose. For with the formation of water, protoplasm (the physical basis of all plants and animals) first became possible, what may be called the life molecule then coming into existence. By it, starting in a simple, lowly way, and growing in complexity with time, all vegetable and animal forms have since been gradually built up. In itself the organic molecule is only a more intricate chemical combination of the same elements of which the inorganic substances which preceded it are composed. . . . There is now no more reason to doubt that plants grew out of chemical affinity than to doubt that stones did. Spontaneous generation is as certain as spontaneous variation, of which it is, in fact, only an expression."

Life, he believed, began in the oceans soon after they had cooled below the boiling point, and spread all over them; seaweeds and trilobites existed in France, Siberia and the Argentine, their nearest relatives being now confined to the tropics; coral reefs, now found only in warm equatorial seas, have left their traces within eight degrees of the pole. This looks as if in paleozoic times the oceans were uniformly warm. The same record he finds in the plants of the carboniferous age. Gigantic ferns and other cryptogams grew to an immense size, with vast rapidity and without stopping, for there are no annual rings of growth, no signs of the effect of seasons, no flowers, and little or no color. "Two attributes of the climate this state of things attests. First, it was warm everywhere with a warmth probably surpassing that of the tropics of to-day; and, second, the light was tempered to a half-light known now only under heavy clouds. And both these conditions were virtually general in locality and continuous in time." In the later volume he adds, to corroborate the general darkness, that many of the earlier trilobites, who lived in shallow water, were blind, while others had colossal eyes.

Various theories have been advanced to explain the carboniferous age, which he reviews, showing why they do not account for the facts. His own is that while the oceans were still hot a vast steaming must have gone up from them, forming clouds of great density that would keep the sun's heat and light out, and the warmth of the Earth in. "In paleozoic times, then, it was the Earth itself, not the Sun, to which plant and animal primarily stood beholden for existence. This gives us a most instructive glimpse into one planetologic process. To the planet's own internal heat is due the chief fostering of the beginnings of life upon its surface." [1]

But he points out that a time must have come when the Earth, and especially its seas, had cooled, the envelope of dense cloud had gradually been pierced, and the sun's rays let in. Then began the sharp alternation of day and night, the changes in the seasons and the diversity of climates, when the palms descended to the tropics, and the flora and fauna as we know them started to develop. This is the period

[1] Since he wrote, the discovery of radio-active substances has given rise to a wholly new crop of theories about the early geologic processes in the Earth's crust.

when the Sun was dominant, or the Sun-Sustained Stage, the one in which we live.

Later the Earth went through another experience of which the facts are well known, but the date and cause have puzzled astronomers and geologists alike, for it lies in the twilight zone between the regions they illuminate. It is the Glacial Periods. He discusses the theory of Croll, once largely accepted but now abandoned, that these periods were due to a change in the eccentricity of the Earth's orbit, combined with a progression of the equinoxes, which so altered the seasons that the northern hemisphere would have summers hot but too short to melt the snow and ice accumulated in the long cold winters. In fact Percival had already reviewed this theory some years before in a paper presented to the American Philosophic Society (Proc. Vol. XXXIX, No. 164) in which he showed that the eccentricity and inclination of axis in Mars are very close to those Croll had attributed to the Earth, and yet a glacial period does not exist there. In the case of Mars it is the southern hemisphere that should be glaciated, but in fact, although that pole has the larger extent of snow in winter this sometimes disappears wholly in the summer, which is never true at the northern pole. If, indeed, the amount of ice formed were much larger it would not be melted, so that the amount of water falling and frozen, and not the eccentricity or inclination of the axis, would be the cause of an ice age.

But he had another reason for rejecting Croll's theory, and, indeed, for disbelieving in a general ice age altogether. It was that the glaciation does not appear to proceed from the pole, but from various distinct centres, moving from them in all directions, north as well as south; while some

places, like northern Siberia, that one would expect to be
covered with ice, were not so covered. Nor was the greater
cold confined to the northern hemisphere, for on some
mountains at the equator, and even at the south pole, there
was more ice and snow than there is to-day. His explanation is that certain parts of the Earth's surface were for some
reason raised higher than they are now; and from the snow
mountains or plateaus so formed the sheets of ice flowed
down.

The remainder of the book on "Mars as the Abode of
Life"—and it is the larger part of it—contains the reasons
for believing that Mars is inhabited, the canals artificial,
and that the Earth will in like manner gradually lose its
supply of water. But this argument need not be retraced
here, because with it the reader has already been made familiar. "The Evolution of Worlds" ends with a chapter
entitled "Death of a World"; for to him the whole theory
of planetary evolution is a vast drama, albeit with a tragic
close. He describes four ways in which a planet, and all life
thereon, may be destroyed. Three of these are: the effect of
tidal action that would bring the same face always toward
the Sun; the loss of water and atmosphere; and the cooling
and final extinction of the Sun. All these things he cheer-
fully reminds us are sure to happen, but at a time enor-
mously distant. The other is a collision with a star—"That
any of the lucent stars, the stars commonly so called, could
collide with the Sun, or come near enough to amount to
the same thing, is demonstrably impossible for aeons of
years. But this is far from the case for a dark star. Such a
body might well be within a hundredth of the distance of
the nearest of our known neighbors. . . . Our senses could

only be cognizant of its proximity by the borrowed light it reflected from our own Sun." A collision of this kind might happen at any time, but he consoles us by saying that "judged by any scale of time we know, the chance of such occurrence is immeasurably remote." In an earlier part of the book he describes what its advent would be:

"We can calculate how much warning we should have of the coming catastrophe. The Sun with its retinue is speeding through space at the rate of eleven miles a second toward a point near the bright star Vega. Since the tramp would probably also be in motion with a speed comparable with our own, it might hit us coming from any point in space, the likelihood depending upon the direction and amount of its own speed. So that at the present moment such a body may be in any part of the sky. But the chances are greatest if it be coming from the direction toward which the Sun is travelling, since it would then be approaching us head on. If it were travelling itself as fast as the Sun, its relative speed of approach would be twenty-two miles a second.

"The previousness of the warning would depend upon the stranger's size. The warning would be long according as the stranger was large. Let us assume it the mass of the Sun, a most probable supposition. Being dark, it must have cooled to a solid, and its density therefore be much greater than the Sun's, probably something like eight times as great, giving it a diameter about half his or four hundred and thirty thousand miles. Its apparent brightness would depend both upon its distance and upon its intrinsic brightness or albedo, and this last would itself vary according to its distance from the Sun. . . . We shall assume, therefore, that its brilliancy would be only that of the Moon, remembering that the last stages of its fateful journey would be much more resplendently set off.

"With these data we can find how long it would be visible before the collision occurred. As a very small telescopic star it would undoubtedly escape detection. It is not likely that the stranger would be noticed simply from its appearance until it had attained the eleventh magnitude. It would then be one hundred and forty-nine astronomical units from the Sun or at five times the distance of Neptune. But its detection would come about not through the eye of the body, but through the eye of the mind. Long before it could have attracted man's attention to itself directly its effects would have betrayed it. Previous, indeed, to its possible showing in any telescope the behavior of the outer planets of the system would have revealed its presence. The far plummet of man's analysis would have sounded the cause of their disturbance and pointed out the point from which that disturbance came. Celestial mechanics would have foretold, as once the discovery of another planet, so now the end of the world. Unexplained perturbations in the motions of the planets, the far tremors of its coming, would have spoken to astronomers as the first heralding of the stranger and of the destruction it was about to bring. Neptune and Uranus would begin to deviate from their prescribed paths in a manner not to be accounted for except by the action of some new force. Their perturbations would resemble those caused by an unknown exterior planet, but with this difference that the period of the disturbance would be exactly that of the disturbed planet's own period of revolution round the Sun.

"Our exterior sentinels might fail thus to give us warning of the foreign body because of being at the time in the opposite parts of their orbits. We should then be first apprised of its coming by Saturn, which would give us less prefatory notice.

"It would be some twenty-seven years from the time it entered the range of vision of our present telescopes before it rose to that of the unarmed eye. It would then have reached forty-nine astronomical units' distance, or two-thirds as far again as Neptune. From here, however, its approach would be more rapid. Humanity by this time would have been made acquainted with its sinister intent from astronomic calculation, and would watch its slow gaining in conspicuousness with ever growing alarm. During the next three years it would have ominously increased to a first magnitude star, and two years and three months more have reached the distance of Jupiter and surpassed by far in lustre Venus at her brightest.

"Meanwhile the disturbance occasioned not simply in the outer planets but in our own Earth would have become very alarming indeed. The seasons would have been already greatly changed, and the year itself lengthened, and all these changes fraught with danger to everything upon the Earth's face would momentarily grow worse. In one hundred and forty-five days from the time it passed the distance of Jupiter it would reach the distance of the Earth. Coming from Vega, it would not hit the Earth or any of the outer planets, as the Sun's way is inclined to the planetary planes by some sixty degrees, but the effects would be none the less marked for that. Day and night alone of our astronomic relations would remain. It would be like going mad and yet remaining conscious of the fact. Instead of following the Sun we should now in whole or part, according to the direction of its approach, obey the stranger. For nineteen more days this frightful chaos would continue; as like some comet glorified a thousand fold the tramp dropped silently upon the Sun. Toward the close of the nineteenth day the catastrophe would occur, and almost in merciful deliverance from the already chaotic cataclysm and the yet greater horror of its contemplation, we should know no more." [2]

[2] It is now practically certain that a dark star would be of very high density and small size, which would make the warning before the catastrophe still shorter.

CHAPTER XVI

INTERLUDES

NATURALLY Percival's observations of Mars, and still more the conclusions he drew from them, provoked widespread attention among astronomers, some of whom were convinced, while some withheld judgment and others were very frankly disbelievers. This did not amaze him, for he felt that new ideas made their way slowly, and had always done so. He met objections, argued his case and expected ultimate acceptance of his views. Perhaps not less naturally the popular interest was also great. Newspapers as well as periodicals all over America, in England, France, Germany and other countries, published and discussed his views, especially, of course, on the existence of intelligent beings on Mars and their artificial canals upon its surface. Marconi was reported as saying that within a few years we should be in wireless communication with them.

Meanwhile his life had been going on at the usual furious pace; lecturing here and there; writing for scientific journals, mostly, but not wholly, on planets, satellites etc.; managing his own property and his father's estate; keeping in constant touch with his computers in Boston and his observers at Flagstaff, worrying over the health of one of them whom he urges to take a vacation and recruit; and also standing his watch as observer himself. A watch it was,

145

"Jupiter before dinner and Mars at 4 A.M." There was also a large correspondence with astronomers and others who were interested in his work. To one of the latter he writes on December 14, 1907: "In answer to your note of Dec. 5, which has been forwarded to me here, I beg to say that the best and final education must always be given by one's self."

Although the canals had already been photographed, he was not yet free from the doubters of the actuality of his observations, for on May 15th of that year we find him writing to Professor Simon Newcomb—then at the height of his great reputation who had suggested that the comparative continuity of the canals was an optical illusion, a long letter giving the reasons for believing that this could not be so, but that they must be as observed.[1] The proof of this he was seeking to make more clear, and in this same year he sent Dr. Slipher, with Professor Todd of Amherst College, on an expedition to the Andes to take more photographs of Mars, which appeared in the *Century* for December.

But it was not all work. The hospitality of the Observatory was kept up; visiting astronomers and friends lent a gayety to the place. Mr. George Agassiz, for example, long his friend in many labors, was there for many months in 1907 and 1909, helping greatly in his observations;[2] the late Professor Edward S. Morse at sundry times, and Pro-

[1] The discussion was continued in the press, Percival's main argument being in his article in the *Astrophysical Journal* for October, 1907. Among those who claimed that the canals were optical illusions was Mr. Douglass after his connection with the Observatory had ceased; although he had previously drawn many of them, and himself discovered those in the darker regions.

[2] In *Popular Science Monthly*, for September, 1907, Mr. Agassiz told his experience in observing at Flagstaff, and why the appearance of canals cannot be due to optical or visual illusions.

fessor Robert W. Willson in 1909 and 1914. He was also in kindly relations with his neighbors, who were "courteous enough to ask me to talk, and I am deep in addresses." In fact some of them were constantly urging him to stand for Senator from the State. He was interested also in children, and in March, 1908, he is sending word to Dr. Slipher about a little girl from Texas eight years old who is to pass through Flagstaff, and asks permission to look through his big telescope as she "just loves astronomy." He was fond of telling about his meeting a negro tending chickens to whom he suggested keeping a watch on them the next day because they would go to roost about eleven o'clock; and they did, for there was an eclipse of the sun. Some days later he met the negro again, who expressed astonishment at his knowing in advance that the chickens would go to roost, and asked if he had known it a week before. Yes, he had known it then. "Did you know it a month before?" "Yes, I knew it a month before." "Did you know it a year before?" "Yes, I knew it a year before." "But those chickens weren't born then!" Had he lived to the present day he might have discovered a resemblance to some tendencies in ideas about the present depression.

Nor were his thoughts confined to this country, for in August, 1905, he writes to a friend: "I go to Japan this autumn, but how and when I have not yet decided." His old interest remained, and in April 1908, he arranged an exhibition in Boston by a Shinto priest of walking over hot coals and up a ladder of sword blades. "The place," he says, "was full and the audience gratified at being asked. While in the distance people outside the pale stood on carts and boys even to the tops of far off houses, one perched on

the tip of a chimney. Dr. Suga cut himself slightly but
not seriously. He did very well considering, though it was
not possible of course for a poor lone priest to come up to
what he might have done in Japan. The rite was beautifully set forth and the setting of the whole enclosure worthy
the most artistic people in the world. Policemen kept out
the crowd and stared aghast, and altogether it was a relished
function."

He probably would have been greatly grieved had he been
told that he would never revisit the land where he had spent
so much of his earlier life and thought; but astronomy was
now his dominant occupation, and was constantly presenting new questions to engross his attention and fill his time.
Yet in the years when Mars was not in opposition this did
not prevent, indeed it rather stimulated, visits to Europe,
where he saw his astronomical friends, and lectured on his
discoveries; for he was a member of the National Astronomic Societies of France and Germany had received from
the former in 1904 the Janssen medal for his researches on
Mars, and in 1907 Mr. Lampland that of the Royal Photographic Society of Great Britain for the work on the planets. We find him across the ocean in the summer of 1906,
lunching with Sir Robert Ball in Cambridge, Deslandres
and Flammarion in Paris, and "pegging away" there at his
lectures.

Two years later, on June 10, 1908, he married Miss Con-
stance Savage Keith, and they went abroad at the end of
the month. When in London they met his first cousin,
A. Lawrence Rotch, the meteorologist, who like him had
established and directed, at his own expense, an observatory
for the study of his subject; in this case on Blue Hill near

Boston. Percival wanted to photograph measurable lines to see how they appeared in a camera from the air. So he went up with his cousin in a balloon, and obtained photographs of the paths in Hyde Park which came out very well. His wife also went up with them; and, what with his reputation, the ascent in a balloon and their recent marriage, the event was too much for a reporter to resist; and there appeared in a newspaper an imaginary picture of an astronomer and a bride in a wedding dress taking their honeymoon in the basket of a balloon. They travelled together in England, Switzerland, Germany and France, and she recalls, when he was giving a lecture at the Sorbonne, a sudden exclamation from a Frenchman directly behind her: "Why! He is even clever in French!"

Mrs. Lowell has written an account of the diligence, the enthusiasm, the hardships of Percival and his colleagues, and the spirit of Flagstaff:

"In October, soon after our return from Europe, I discovered that the scientist's motto is—"Time is sacred." I was to meet him on the train for Flagstaff leaving the South Station at 2 P.M.; anxious to impress him with my reputation for being punctual, I boarded the train about ten minutes before two. Percival came into the car, holding his watch in his hand, just about two minutes before two. He turned to me: "What time were you here?" I answered triumphantly: "Oh, I got here about ten minutes ago." His reply was: "I consider that just as unpunctual as to be late. Think how much could have been accomplished in ten minutes!" I have never forgotten that remark. Percival never wasted minutes.

"Late in the afternoon of the third day, as we were nearing

Flagstaff, through the dusk we could see that there had been a heavy fall of snow, so deep that when the train stopped our Pullman, being far in the rear, was where the snow—not having been shovelled—was almost level with the upper step. The men from the Observatory were there, and their first words were 'Seeing Good.' Percival jumped into the deep snow, and taking Mr. E. C. Slipher with him, drove to the telescope.

"Astronomers take much for granted so far as the details of domestic life are concerned, and I made up my mind to be a help and not a hindrance. Dr. V. M. Slipher's wife came to the rescue, and under her supervision things were soon adjusted even to a hot supper and preparation for breakfast the next morning. She was, and always is, a wonder. Though the wife be not an astronomer a happy asset is it if she can appreciate her husband's work, his sacrifices and self-denials. Many times have I seen their frost-bitten ears and thumbs; hungry and tired men, but never complaining—patience personified. They are slaves to the laws that rule the celestial.

"The house we lived in on Mars Hill was a long rambling one, both roof and sides shingled. Inside all but two rooms were finished, and partitioned. Two were papered; one of them I papered because no paper hanger happened to be in town. Occasionally Percival would come in to see how the work was progressing, and help by steadying the ladder or stirring the paste. The sitting room—or den, as it was referred to more often—was lined with half logs from which the bark had not been stripped. In the ceiling were logs used as beams. During the evening, when all was quiet, one might hear insects busily working out some scheme of their own. Open spaces were beamed and, as the logs did not exactly fit, through the spaces trade-rats would descend from the attic.

"To love nature, and the one for whom one works, it matters not where one is; that is what one realizes when on Mars Hill. One learns to go without things. They seem of such minor importance to that for which the men are seeking; one gets ashamed of oneself to think otherwise. Each man moves with a definite purpose, indefatigable workers, no thought of themselves when skies are clear, always watching, cold or torrid heat makes no difference, work goes on just the same.

"I became deeply impressed with the necessity of obedience to laws. I said once to Percival that I had been asked if it were true that he was an atheist, a non-believer. His answer was that he believed in keeping the laws; what chaos would happen if they were not. Often he would quote passages from the Bible—Genesis I, 14-20. The laws made on Mount Sinai, he said, are still the same laws to obey. To live in the atmosphere of such men accomplishing great things, deprived of many material comforts, makes one feel humble and spurs one on to 'Help and not to hinder.'

"Servants we often had to do without. They would come out with us, and then after a few days, learning of the nearness to the Pacific coast, the lure of California would bring from them some lame excuse to leave, at once! To obtain others, when none were to be had in the town, I would have to go to Los Angeles. Finally, after several had left, I persuaded Percival to let me try to do the cooking; and later he would refer to that time as happy peaceful days. With the help of the kind wives, Mrs. Slipher and Mrs.

Lampland, I learned much, how to make bread and soup,— two very essential articles in our household,—and to get up camping outfits and quick meals for unexpected guests.

"Lonesome, monotonous—never. Distant as Mars Hill may be from large cities, something of interest was happening continually. The State Normal School of Arizona is in the town, and on certain nights classes of students were brought up the hill to look through the telescope. Flagstaff is on the main line of the Santa Fe. There were three incoming trains from the East each day, and as many from the West, and many people stop off there to visit the different points of interest, the Lowell Observatory being one.

"In August, 1910, a group of astronomers, representing the International Union for Coöperation in Solar Research, debarked from the train, on their way to Pasadena; Professor Herbert H. Turner from England among them. He it was who many years later suggested for Percival's 'Planet X' the name Pluto. The group, of about thirty, arrived by the first morning train and stayed at the Observatory until the last train left at night. The one thing that I was successful in getting enough of for lunch and dinner was watermelon. It proved a happy hit; for a year or two afterward, when telling how much they enjoyed their visit, the watermelons were spoken of as being such a treat. It was a hot day and the melons were cold; probably that explained their enthusiasm.

"One Christmas we invited all the children of Flagstaff to come to the Observatory for a Christmas tree and supper. Percival dressed as Santa Claus and spoke to them down the chimney; then he came down into the Library where they were gathered about the tree, and gave a present and candy to every child. That was twenty-seven years ago. When I was in Flagstaff this spring, the little child I had held in my lap while Percival read 'The Night Before Christmas' came to speak to me and told me never would she forget that Christmas, and that her two little children repeatedly asked her to tell them the story of that Christmas and all that happened at the Santa Claus party on Mars Hill."

In a recent letter to Mrs. Lowell, Dr. Lampland also gives a glimpse into Percival's life at Flagstaff; and though written to refresh her recollections she preferred to insert it as it stands.

"Fresh in memory and pleasant to recall are your many visits to Flagstaff and your activities at the Observatory, where you were designing and supervising architect, carrying through the additions to the director's residence, the garage, and the new administration building. And I also remember your valued help to us in connection with the house in which we live and your telegram 'Mr. Lowell gives benediction and sanction to plans. Proceed.'"

He then goes on to tell of Percival's friends from both West and East, and continues:

"You remember he was an enthusiastic gardener and always had a garden here at the Observatory. He had great success with many flowers and I recall especially fine displays of hollyhocks, zinnias, and a considerable variety of bulbs. Gourds, squashes and pumpkins were also great favorites. You will remember one year the especially fine collection of gourds and that bumper crop of huge pumpkins, many prize specimens being sugar fed. At times Dr. Lowell could be seen in the short intervals he took for outdoor recreation, busy with his little camel's hair brush pollenizing some of the flowers. And perhaps you will remember the little record book lying on the back veranda containing his observations of the daily growth of the diameter of the gourds, all measured carefully with little calipers. Then the frequent, almost daily, walks on the mesa. Certainly he knew all the surrounding country better than anyone here. He would refer to the different places such as Wolf Canyon, Amphitheatre Canyon, Indian Paint Brush Ridge, Holly Ravine, Mullein Patch, etc. In these walks he seemed to be constantly observing something new and of course trees, flowers, and wild life always interested him. Trees were an endless source of interest to him and he took many trips to more distant localities for these studies. Cedars or junipers seemed to be favorite subjects for study, though other varieties or kinds were not overlooked. An oak and an ash were named after him, new species that were discovered on the Observatory mesa and in Sycamore Canyon.

"At every season of the year he always found something in wild life to fascinate him, and you will remember his observations and notes of butterflies, birds, squirrels, rabbits, coyotes, deer and other inhabitants of the mesa. These friends must never be disturbed or harmed. But it was permissible to hunt with a camera! And he himself delighted with his kodak, photographing footprints, etc., and often attempting to get exposures of the creatures themselves. The Observatory grounds were a sanctuary for wild life.

"For many of us an interesting side of eminent personages is to know something about their activities, such for example as reading, outside of their professional occupations. In Dr. Lowell's case you should find ample opportunity to treat a subject that will not admit of monotony. It would seem that practically every field of knowledge interested him. For the lighter reading as a relaxing and restful diversion you will remember the full bookshelves of detective stories, travel, exploration, etc. Accounts of adventure and discoveries, if well written, were welcome to his list of miscellaneous reading. The Latin classics were always near at hand, and widely and well had he read them, and much were they prized as friends in his later life.

"As you know, it is not easy for the observing astronomer to lead a strictly regular life in that the hours at the telescope often make it necessary to use, for the much needed rest, part of the daily hours usually given to work. His intense occupation with his research problems, however, was broken with great regularity for short intervals before lunch and dinner. These times of recreation were given to walks on the mesa or work in the garden. When night came, if he was not occupied at the telescope, he was generally to be found in his den. It was not always possible for him to lay aside his research problems at this time of the day, but he did have some wholesome views on the necessity of recreation and a necessary amount of leisure to prevent a person from falling into the habit of the 'grind.' To those who came to his den the picture of some difficult technical work near his chair, such as Tisserand's *Mechanique Celeste* will be recalled, though he might at the time be occupied with reading of a lighter character. And occasionally during the evening he might be seen consulting certain difficult parts upon which he was pondering. . . .

"The famous outing to the White Mountains was often the subject of much amusement at the dinner parties when Dr. Lowell and Judge Doe were both there. In later years that famous expedition seemed to be an inexhaustible source of fun—the voracious mosquitoes, the discomforts of a camp and beds under water, atrocious coffee, and so on!!

"And this reminds me of many dinner parties on Dr. Lowell's and Judge Doe's birthdays. These were jolly gatherings, and the brilliant repartee passing between Dr. Lowell and the Judge was a great delight to those who were present.

"Many things about the place often remind me of the intensely busy days before Dr. Lowell passed away. There were several excursions for his tree studies, to Sycamore Canyon, an arduous trip, and to other localities near Flagstaff for further studies of different species of junipers in their native habitat. The specimens were carefully sorted and packed for Professor Sargent of the Arnold Arboretum. Then I remember helping him plant many bulbs on the last two days before he was fatally stricken. The squills he planted at that time in the little bed under the oak tree near the entrance of the B. M. return every spring." [3]

[3] The Director's house was commonly known as "The Baronial Mansion."

CHAPTER XVII

THE EFFECT OF COMMENSURATE PERIODS

The Asteroids and Saturn's Rings

Ever inquiring, ever fertile, his mind turned to seek the explanation of divers astronomical phenomena. In 1912, for example, under the title "Precession and the Pyramids," we find him discussing in the *Popular Science Monthly* the pyramid of Cheops as an astronomical observatory, with its relation to the position of the star then nearest to the North Pole, its lines of light and shadow, in a great gallery constructed with the object of recording the exact changes in the seasons.

But leaving aside these lesser interests, and the unbroken systematic observation of the planets, his attention in the later years of his life was chiefly occupied by two subjects, not unconnected, but which may be described separately. They are, first, the influence over each other's position and orbits of two bodies, both revolving about a far larger one; and, second, the search for an outer planet beyond the path of Neptune. Each of these studies involved the use of mathematics with expanding series of equations which no one had better attempt to follow unless he is fresh and fluent in such forms of expression. For accurate and quantitative results they are absolutely essential, but an impression of what he was striving to do may be given without them.

Two bodies revolving about a common centre at different distances, and therefore different rates of revolution, will sometimes be on the same side of the central body, and thus nearer together; sometimes on opposite sides, when they will be much farther apart. Now it is clear that the attraction of gravity, being inversely as the square of the distance, will be greatest when they are nearest together; and if this happens at the same point in their orbits every time they approach each other the effect will be cumulative, and in the aggregate much larger than if they approach at different parts of their orbits and hence pull each other sometimes in one direction and sometimes in another. To use a homely, and not altogether apt, illustration: If a man, starting from his front door, walk every day across his front lawn in the same track he will soon make a beaten path and wear the grass away. If, instead, he walk by this path only every other day and on the alternate days by another, he will make two paths, neither of which will be so much worn. If he walk by three tracks in succession the paths will be still less worn; and if he never walk twice in the same place the effect on the grass will be imperceptible.

Now, if the period taken by the outer body to complete its orbit be just twice as long as that taken by the inner, they will not come close together again until the outer one has gone round once to the inner one's twice, and they will always approach at the same point in their orbits. Hence the effects on each other will be greatest. If the outer one take just two turns while the inner takes three they will approach again only at the same point, but less frequently; so that the pull will be always the same, but repeated less often. This will be clearly true whenever the rates of the revolution differ by unity: *e.g.,* 1 to 2, 2 to 3, 3 to 4, 4 to 5, etc.

Take another case where the periods differ by two; for example, where the inner body revolves about the central one three times while the outer one does so once; in that case the inner one will catch up with the outer when the latter has completed half a revolution and the inner one and a half; and again when the outer has completed one whole revolution and the inner three. In this case there will be two strong pulls on opposite sides of the orbits, and, as these pulls are not the same, the total effect will be less than if there were only one pull in one direction. This is true whenever the periods of revolution differ by two, *e.g.,* 1 to 3, 3 to 5, 5 to 7. If the periods differ by three the two bodies will approach three times,—once at the starting point, then one third way round, and again two thirds way round, before they reach the starting point; three different pulls clearly less effective.

In cases like these, where the two bodies approach in only a limited number of places in their orbits the two periods of revolution are called commensurate, because their ratio is expressed by a simple fraction. The effect is greater as the number of such places in the orbit is less, and as the number of revolutions before they approach is less. But it is clearly greater than when the two bodies approach always at different places in their orbits, never again where they have done so before. This is when the two periods are incommensurate, so that their ratio cannot be expressed by any vulgar fraction. One other point must be noticed. The commensurate orbit, and hence the distance from the Sun, and the period of revolution, of the smaller and therefore most affected body, may not be far from a distance where the orbits would be incommensurate. To take the most completely incommensurate ratio known to science, that of the diameter of a circle to the circumference, which has been carried out to seven hundred decimal places without repetition of the figures. This is expressed by the decimal fraction .314159 etc. and yet this differs from the simple commensurate 1/3 or .333333 etc. by only about five per cent.; so that a smaller body may have to be pulled by the larger, only a very short way before it reaches a point where it will be seriously affected no more.

The idea that commensurateness affects the mutual attraction of bodies, and hence the perturbations in their orbits, especially of the smaller one, was not new; but Percival carried it farther, and to a greater degree of accuracy, by observation, by mathematics and in its applications. The most obvious example of its effects lay in the influence of Jupiter upon the distribution of the asteroids, that almost innumerable collection of small bodies revolving about the Sun between the orbits of Jupiter and Mars, of which some six hundred had been discovered. These are so small, compared with Jupiter, that, not only individually but in the aggregate, their influence upon it may be disregarded, and only its effect upon them be considered. In its immediate neighborhood the commensurate periods, Percival points out, come so close together (100 to 101, 99 to 100, etc.) that although occasions of approach would be infrequent they would be enough in time to disturb any bodies so near, until the planet had cleared out everything in its vicinity that did not, by revolving around it, become its own satellite.

Farther off Jupiter's commensurate zones are less frequent, but where they occur the fragments revolving about the Sun would be so perturbed by the attraction of the planet as to be displaced, mainly, as Percival points out, to the sunward side. This has made gaps bare of such fragments, and between them incommensurate spaces where they could move freely in their solar orbits. Here they might have gathered in a nucleus and, collecting other fragments to it, form a small planet, were it not that the gaps were frequent enough to prevent nuclei of sufficient size arising anywhere. Thus the asteroids remained a host of little bodies revolving about the Sun, with gaps in their ranks—as he puts it "embryos of planets destined never to be born."

The upper diagram in the plate opposite page 166 shows the distribution and relative densities of the asteroids, with the gaps at the commensurate points. The plate is taken from his "Memoir on Saturn's Rings," [1] and brings us to another study of commensurate periods with quite a different set of bodies obeying the same law. Indeed, among the planets observed at Flagstaff not the least interesting was Saturn, and its greatest peculiarity was its rings.

In Bulletin No. 32 of the Observatory (Nov. 24, 1907) Percival had written: "Laplace first showed that the rings could not be, as they appear, wide solid rings inasmuch as the strains due to the differing attraction of Saturn for the several parts must disrupt them. Peirce then proved that even a series of very narrow solid rings could not subsist and that

[1] Memoirs of the Lowell Observatory, Vol. I, No. II.

the rings must be fluid. Finally Clerk-Maxwell showed that even this was not enough and that the rings to be stable must be made up of discrete particles, a swarm of meteorites in fact. But, if my memory serves me right, Clerk-Maxwell himself pointed out that even such a system could not eternally endure but was bound eventually to be forced both out and in, a part falling upon the surface of the planet, a part going to form a satellite farther away.

"Even before this Edward Roche in 1848 had shown that the rings must be composed of discrete particles, mere dust and ashes. He drew this conclusion from his investigations on the minimum distance at which a fluid satellite could revolve around its primary without being disrupted by tidal strains.

"The dissolution which Clerk-Maxwell foresaw can easily be proved to be inevitable if the particles composing the swarm are not at considerable distances from one another, which is certainly not the case with the rings as witnessed by the light they send us even allowing for their comminuted form. For a swarm of particles thus revolving round a primary are in stable equilibrium *only in the absence of collisions*. Now in a crowded company collisions due either to the mutual pulls of the particles or to the perturbations of the satellites must occur. At each collision although the moment of momentum remains the same, energy is lost unless the bodies be perfectly elastic, a condition not found in nature, the lost energy being converted into heat. In consequence some particles will be forced in toward the planet while others are driven out and eventually the ring system disappears.

"Now the interest of the observations at Flagstaff consists

in their showing us this disintegration in process of taking place and furthermore in a way that brings before us an interesting case of celestial mechanics."

He examines the rings mathematically, as the result of perturbations caused by the two nearest of the planet's satellites, Mimas and Enceladus.

The effect is the same that occurs in the case of Jupiter and the asteroids, Saturn taking the place of the Sun, his satellites that of Jupiter, and the rings that of the asteroids. In spite of repetition it may be well to state in his own words the principle of commensurate periods and its application to the rings: [2]

"The same thing can be seen geometrically by considering that the two bodies have their greatest perturbing effect on one another when in conjunction and that if the periods of the two be commensurate they will come to conjunction over and over in these same points of the orbit and thus the disturbance produced by one on the other be cumulative. If the periods are not commensurate the conjunctions will take place in ever shifting positions and a certain compensation be effected in the outstanding results. In proportion as the ratio of periods is simple will the perturbation be potent. Thus with the ratio 1:2 the two bodies will approach closest only at one spot and always there until the perturbations induced themselves destroy the commensurability of period. With 1:3 they will approach at two different spots recurrently; with 1:4 at three, and so on. . . .

"We see, then, that perturbations, which in this case will result in collisions, must be greatest on those particles which have periods commensurate with those of the satellites. But

[2] Bulletin No. 32.

inasmuch as there are many particles in any cross-section of
the ring there must be a component of motion in any collision tending to throw the colliding particles out of the
plane of the ring, either above or below it.

"Considering, now, those points where commensurability
exists between the periods of particle and satellite we find
these in the order of their potency:

With Mimas, 1:2

1:3

1:4

With Enceladus, 1:3

2:3 of Mimas and 1:2; 2:3 of Enceladus falling outside
the ring system. 1:2 of Mimas and 1:3 of Enceladus fall in
Cassini's division, which separates ring A from ring B. . . .
1:3 of Mimas' period falls at the boundary of ring B and
ring C at 1:50 radii of Saturn from the centre."

In the following years this supposition was reinforced by
the discovery of six new divisions in the rings. Three of
them were in ring A and three in ring B, two of them in each
case seen by Percival for the first time. This led to very
careful measurements of Saturn's ball and rings in 1913–14
and again in 1915; recorded in Bulletins 66 and 68 of the
Observatory. Careful allowance was made for irradiation,
and the results checked by having two sets of measurements,
one made by Percival, the other by Mr. E. C. Slipher. The
observations were, of course, made when the rings were
so tilted to the Earth as to show very widely, the tilt on
March 21, 1915, showing them at their widest for fifteen
years.

But unfortunately, as it seemed, the divisions in the rings

did not come quite where the commensurate ratios with the two nearest satellites should place them. They came in the right order and nearly where they ought to be, but always a little farther from Saturn. It occurred to Percival that this might be due to an error in the calculation of the motion of the rings, that if the attraction of Saturn were slightly more than had been supposed the revolutions of all parts of the rings would be slightly faster, and the places in them where the periods would be commensurate with the satellites would be slightly farther out, that is where the divisions actually occur. Everyone knows that the earth is not a perfect sphere but slightly elliptical, or oblate, contracted from pole to pole and enlarged at the equator; and the same is even more true of Saturn on account of its greater velocity of rotation. Now its attraction on bodies as near it as the rings, and to a less extent on its satellites, is a little greater than it would be if it were a perfect uniform sphere; and it would be greater still if it were not uniform throughout, but composed of layers increasing in density, in rapidity of rotation, and hence in oblateness, toward the centre. Percival made, therefore, a highly intricate calculation on what the attraction of such a body would be ("Observatory Memoir on Saturn's Rings," Sept. 7, 1915), and found that it accounted almost exactly for the discrepancy between the points of computed commensurateness and the observed divisions in the rings. Such a constitution of Saturn is by no means improbable in view of its still fluid condition and the process of contraction that it is undergoing. He found it noteworthy that a study of the perturbations of the rings by the satellites should bring to light the invisible constitution of the planet itself:

"Small discrepancies are often big with meaning. Just as

the more accurate determination of the nitrogen content of the air led Sir William Ramsay to the discovery of argon; so these residuals between the computed and the observed features of *Saturn's* rings seem to lead to a new conception of *Saturn's* internal constitution. That the mere position of his rings should reveal something within him which we cannot see may well appear as singular as it is significant." (p. 5); and he concludes: (pp. 20–22).

"All this indicates that *Saturn* has not yet settled down to a uniform rotation. Not only in the spots we see is the rate different for different spots but from this investigation it would appear that the speed of its spin increases as one sinks from surface to centre.[3]

"The subject of this memoir is of course two-fold: first, the observed discrepancy, and second, the theory to account for it. The former demands explanation and the latter seems the only way to satisfy it. From the positions of the divisions in its rings we are thus led to believe that *Saturn* is actually rotating in layers with different velocities, the inside ones turning the faster. If these layers were two only, or substantially two, this would result in *Saturn's* being composed of a very oblate kernel surrounded by a less oblate husk of cloud."

The divisions so made in Saturn's rings by its satellites may be seen in the lower of the two diagrams opposite; the three fractions followed by an E indicating the divisions

---

[3] In a recent letter from the Observatory Mr. E. C. Slipher describes a great white spot that appeared on the equator of Saturn in 1933. It behaved as of hot matter flung up from the interior, and after two or three days spread itself towards the East in the direction of the planet's rotation. His explanation is that the level from which this matter came is revolving faster than the atmospheric shell, the new material coming to the visible surface constantly more and more in advance of the original spot—a confirmation of Percival's calculations.

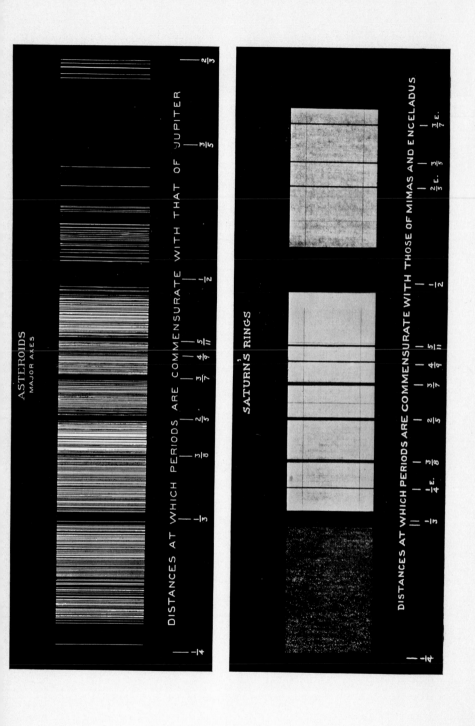

ASTEROIDS
MAJOR AXES

DISTANCES AT WHICH PERIODS ARE COMMENSURATE WITH THAT OF JUPITER

$\frac{1}{4}$ $\frac{1}{3}$ $\frac{3}{8}$ $\frac{2}{5}$ $\frac{3}{7}$ $\frac{4}{9}$ $\frac{5}{11}$ $\frac{1}{2}$ $\frac{3}{5}$ $\frac{2}{3}$

SATURN'S RINGS

DISTANCES AT WHICH PERIODS ARE COMMENSURATE WITH THOSE OF MIMAS AND ENCELADUS

$\frac{1}{4}$ $\frac{1}{3}$ $\frac{1}{4}$ E. $\frac{3}{8}$ $\frac{2}{5}$ $\frac{3}{7}$ $\frac{4}{9}$ $\frac{5}{11}$ $\frac{1}{2}$ $\frac{2}{5}$ E. $\frac{3}{5}$ $\frac{1}{3}$ E.

caused by Enceladus, the rest those caused by Mimas. The upper diagram represents, as already remarked, the similar effects by Jupiter on the asteroids. A slight inspection shows their coincidence.

CHAPTER XVIIII

THE ORIGIN OF THE PLANETS

In a paper presented to the American Academy in April, 1913, and printed in their Memoirs [1] Percival explained the "Origin of the Planets" by the same principle of commensurate periods. In addition to what has already been said about the places where these periods occur coming closer and closer together as an object nears the planet, so that it is enabled to draw neighboring small bodies into itself, he points out that in attracting any object outside of its own orbit a planet is acting from the same side as the Sun thereby increasing the Sun's attraction, accelerating the motion of the particle and making it come sunward. Whereas on a particle inside its orbit the planet is acting against the Sun, thereby diminishing its attraction, slowing the motion of the particle and causing it to move outward. "Thus a body already formed tends to draw surrounding matter to itself by making that matter's mean motion nearly synchronous with its own." These two facts, the close—almost continuous—commensurate points, and the effects on the speed of revolution of particles outside and inside its own orbit, assist a nucleus once formed to sweep clear the space so far as its influence is predominant, drawing all matter there to itself, until it has attained its full size. "Any difference of density in

[1] Vol. XIV, No. 1.

a revolving nebula is thus a starting point for accumulation. So soon as two or three particles have gathered together they tend by increased mass to annex their neighbors. An embryo planet is thus formed. By the same principle it grows crescendo through an ever increasing sphere of influence until the commensurate points are too far apart to bridge by their oscillation the space between them."

So much for the process of forming a planet; but what he was seeking was why the planets formed just where they did. For this purpose he worked out intricate mathematical formulae, based on those already known but more fully and exactly developed. These it is not necessary to follow, for the results may be set forth,—so far as possible in his own words. "Beyond a certain distance from the planet the commensurate-period swings no longer suffice to bridge the intervening space and the planet's annexing power stops. This happens somewhat before a certain place is reached where three potent periodic ratios succeed each other— 1:2, 2:5, 1:3. For here the distances between the periodic points is greatly increased. . . .

"At this distance a new action sets in. Though the character of its occasioning be the same it produces a very different outcome. The greater swing of the particles at these commensurate points together with a temporary massing of some of them near it conduces to collisions and near approaches between them which must end in a certain permanent combining there. A nucleus of consolidation is thus formed. This attracts other particles to it, gaining force by what it feeds on, until out of the once diffused mass a new planet comes into being which in its turn gathers to itself the matter about it.

"A new planet tends to collect here: because the annexing power of the old has here ceased while at the same time the scattered constituents to compose it are here aided to combine by the very potent commensurability perturbations of its already formed neighbor.

"So soon as it has come into being another begins to be beyond it, called up in the same manner. It could not do so earlier because the most important *deus ex machina* in the matter, the perturbation of its predecessor, was lacking.

"So the process goes on, each planet acting as a sort of elder sister in bringing up the next.

"That such must have been the genesis of the several planets is evident when we consider that had each arisen of itself out of surrounding matter there would have been in celestial mechanics nothing to prevent their being situated in almost any relative positions other than the peculiar one in which they actually stand. . . .

"It will be noticed that the several planets are not quite at the commensurate points. They are in fact all just inside them. . . . Suppose now a particle or planet close to the commensurable point inside it. The mean motion in consequence of the above perturbation will be permanently increased, and therefore the major axis be permanently decreased. In other words, the particle or planet will be pushed sunward. If it be still where" the effect of the commensurateness is still felt "it will suffer another push, and so on until it has reached a place where the perturbation is no longer sensible." He then goes on to show from his formulae that if the particle were just within the outer edge of the place where the perturbation began to be effective it would also be pushed sunward, and so across the commensurable point until it joined those previously displaced.

"We thus reach from theory two conclusions:

"1. All the planets were originally forced to form where the important and closely lying commensurable points 1:2, 2:5, or 1:3, and in one case 3:5, existed with their neighbors; which of these points it was being determined by the perturbations themselves.

"2. Each planet was at the same time pushed somewhat sunward by pertubation."

He then calculates the mutual perturbations of the major axes of the outer planets taken in pairs and of Venus and the Earth.

"From them we note that:

"1. The inner planet is *caeteris paribus* more potent than the outer.

"2. The greater the mass of the disturber and, in certain cases, the greater the excentricity of either the disturber or the disturbed the greater the effect."

As he points out, the effect of each component of the pair is masked by the simultaneous action of the other, and refers to the case of Jupiter and the asteroids, where the effect they have upon it is imperceptible, and we can see its effect upon them clearly.

Thus he shows that a new planet would naturally arise near to a point where its orbit would be commensurate with that of the older one next to it. But the particular commensurate fraction in each case is not so certain. In general it would depend upon the ratio of the two pulls to each other, for if "the action of the more potent planet greatly exceeds the other's it sweeps to itself particles farther away than would otherwise be possible"; if it does not so greatly exceed it would not sweep them from so far and hence allow the other planet to form nearer. Now of the four commensurate ratios mentioned, near which a planet may form its neighbor, that of 3:5 means that the two planets are relatively nearest together, for the inner one makes only five revolutions while the outer makes three, that is the inner one revolves around the Sun less than twice as fast as the outer one. The ratio 1:2 means that the inner one revolves just twice as fast as the outer; while 2:5 means that it revolves twice and a half as fast, and 1:3 that it does so three times as fast. Thus the nearer equal the pulls of any pair of forming planets the larger the fraction and the nearer the relative distance between them. Relative, mind, for as we go away from the Sun all the dimensions increase and the actual distances between the planets among the rest.

Venus is smaller than the Earth, but her interior position gives her an advantage more than enough to make up for this, with the result that the pulls of the two are more nearly equal than those of any other pair, the commensurate ratio being 3:5. The next nearest equality of pull is between Uranus and Neptune, where the commensurate ratio is 1:2; the next between Jupiter and Saturn, and Venus and Mercury, where it is 2:5; the least equality being between Saturn and Uranus, where it is only 1:3. Mars seems exceptional for, as Percival says, from the mutual pulls we should expect its ratio with the Earth to be 1:3 instead of 1:2 as it is, and he suggests as the explanation, "the continued action of the gigantic Jupiter in this territory, or it may be that a second origin of condensation started with the Earth while Jupiter fashioned the outer planets."

He brings the Memoir to an end with the following summary:

"From the foregoing some interesting deductions are possible:

"1. The planets grew out of scattered material. For had they arisen from already more or less complete nuclei these could not have borne to one another the general comensurate relation of mean motions existent to-day.

"2. Each brought the next one into being by the perturbation it induced in the scattered material at a definite distance from it.

"3. Jupiter was the starting point, certainly as regards the major planets; and is the only one among them that could have had a nucleus at the start, though that, too, may equally have been lacking.

"4. After this was formed Saturn, then Uranus, and then Neptune." (This he shows from the densities of these planets.)

"5. The asteroids point unmistakably to such a genesis, missed in the making.

"6. The inner planets betray *inter se* the action of the same law, and dovetail into the major ones through the 2:5 relation between Mars and the asteroids.

"We thus close with the law we enunciated: *Each planet has formed the next in the series at one of the adjacent commensurable-period points, corresponding to 1:2, 2:5, 1:3, and in one instance 3:5, of its mean motion, each then displacing the other slightly sunward, thus making of the solar system an articulated whole, an inorganic organism, which not only evolved but evolved in a definite order, the steps of which celestial mechanics enables us to retrace.*

"The above planetary law may perhaps be likened to Mendelief's law for the elements. It, too, admits of prediction. Thus in conclusion I venture to forecast that when the nearest trans-Neptunian planet is detected it will be found to have a major axis of very approximately 47.5 astronomical units, and from its position a mass comparable with that of Neptune, though probably less; while, if it follows a feature of the satellite systems which I have pointed out elsewhere, its excentricity should be considerable, with an inclination to match."

The last paragraph we shall have reason to recall again.

This paper on the "Origin of the Planets" has been called the most speculative of Percival's astronomical studies, and so it is; but it fascinated him, and is interesting not more in itself, than as an illustration of the inquiring and imaginative trend of his mind and of the ease with which intricate mathematical work came to the aid of an idea.

Meanwhile his reputation was growing in Europe. At the end of 1909 he is asked to send to the German National Museum in Munich some transparencies of his fundamental work on Mars and other planets with Dr. Slipher's star spectra, and Dr. Max Wolf of Heidelberg who writes the letter adds: "I believe there is no American astronomer, except yours, [sic] invited till now to do so." A year later the firm in Jena which had just published a translation of his "Soul of the Far East" wants to do the same for "Mars as the Abode of Life." In August 1914 he writes to authorize a second French edition of this last book which had been published with the title "Evolution des Mondes." Every other year, he took a vacation of a few weeks in Europe to visit his astronomic friends, and to speak at their societies.

We have seen how he did so after his marriage in 1908. He went with Mrs. Lowell again in the spring of 1910, giving lectures before the Société Astronomique in Paris, and the Royal Institution in London, and once more, two years later, when we find him entertained and speaking before several scientific bodies in both Paris and London. That autumn he was confined to the house by illness; and although he improved and went to Flagstaff in March, he writes of himself in August 1913 as "personally still on the retired list." In the spring it was thought wise for him to take another vacation abroad; and since his wife was recovering from an operation he went alone. He saw his old friends in France and England and enjoyed their hospitality; but he did not feel well, and save for showing at the Bureau des Longitudes "some of our latest discoveries" he seems to have made no addresses. He sailed back on the *Mauretania* on August 1, just before England declared war, and four days later she was instructed to run to Halifax, which she did, reaching it the following day.

That was destined to be his last voyage, for although he seemed well again he was working above his strength. His time in these years was divided between Flagstaff, where his days and nights were spent in observing and calculating, and Boston, where the alternative was between calculations and business. He was always busy and when one summer he hired a house at Marblehead near to his cousins Mr. and Mrs. Guy Lowell he would frequently drop in to see them; and was charming when he did so; but could not spare the time to take a meal there, and never stayed more than five minutes.

CHAPTER XIX

THE SEARCH FOR A TRANS-NEPTUNIAN PLANET

WE must now return to the last paragraph of his "Memoir on the Origin of the Planets," where he suggests the probable distance of a body beyond Neptune. In fact he had long been interested in its existence and whereabouts. By 1905 his calculations had given him so much encouragement that the Observatory began to search for the outer planet, which he then expected would be like Neptune, low in density, large and bright, and therefore much more easily detected than it turned out to be. But the photographs taken in 1906, with a well planned routine search the next year revealed nothing, and he became distrustful of the data on which he was working. In March 1908, one finds in his letter-books from the office in Boston the first of a series of letters to Mr. William T. Garrigan of the Naval Observatory and Nautical Almanack about the residuals of Uranus—that is the residue in the perturbations of its normal orbit not accounted for by those due to the known planets. He suggests including later data than had hitherto been done; asks what elements other astronomers had taken into account in estimating the residuals; points out that for different periods they are made up on different theories in the publications of Greenwich Observatory, and that some curious facts appear from them.

About his own calculation he writes on December 28, 1908: "The results so far are both interesting and promising." He was hard at work on the calculations for such a planet, based upon the residuals of Uranus, and assisted by a corps of computers, with Miss Elizabeth Williams, now Mrs. George Hall Hamilton of the Observatory at Mandeville, Jamaica, at their head.

Before trying to explain the process by which he reached his results it may be well to give his own account of the discovery of Neptune by a similar method: [1]

"Neptune has proved a planet of surprises. Though its orbital revolution is performed direct, its rotation apparently takes place backward, in a plane tilted about 35° to its orbital course. Its satellite certainly travels in this retrograde manner. Then its appearance is unexpectedly bright, while its spectrum shows bands which as yet, for the most part, defy explanation, though they state positively the vast amount of its atmosphere and its very peculiar constitution. But first and not least of its surprises was its discovery,—a set of surprises, in fact. For after owing recognition to one of the most brilliant mathematical triumphs, it turned out not to be the planet expected.

" 'Neptune is much nearer the Sun than it ought to be,' is the authoritative way in which a popular historian puts the intruding planet in its place. For the planet failed to justify theory by not fulfilling Bode's law, which Leverrier and Adams, in pointing out the disturber of Uranus, assumed 'as they could do no otherwise.' Though not strictly correct, as not only did both geometers do otherwise, but neither did otherwise enough, the quotation may serve to bring Bode's

[1] "The Evolution of Worlds," p. 118 and *seq.*

law into court, as it was at the bottom of one of the strangest
and most generally misunderstood chapters in celestial mechanics.

"Very soon after Uranus was recognized as a planet, ap-
proximate ephemerides of its motion resulted in showing
that it had several times previously been recorded as a fixed
star. Bode himself discovered the first of these records, one
by Mayer in 1756, and Bode and others found another made
by Flamsteed in 1690. These observations enabled an elliptic
orbit to be calculated which satisfied them all. Subsequently
others were detected. Lemonnier discovered that he had
himself not discovered it several times, cataloguing it as a
fixed star. Flamsteed was spared a like mortification by being dead. For both these observers had recorded it two or
more nights running, from which it would seem almost incredible not to have suspected its character from its change
of place.

"Sixteen of these pre-discovery observations were found
(there are now nineteen known), which with those made
upon it since gave a series running back a hundred and
thirty years, when Alexis Bouvard prepared his tables of the
planet, the best up to that time, published in 1821. In doing
so, however, he stated that he had been unable to find any
orbit which would satisfy both the new and the old observations. He therefore rejected the old as untrustworthy, for-
getting that they had been satisfied thirty years before, and
based his tables solely on the new, leaving it to posterity, he
said, to decide whether the old observations were faulty or
whether some unknown influence had acted on the planet.
He had hardly made this invidious distinction against the
accuracy of the ancient observers when his own tables began

to be out and grew seriously more so, so that within eleven years they quite failed to represent the planet.

"The discrepancies between theory and observation attracted the attention of the astronomic world, and the idea of another planet began to be in the air. The great Bessel was the first to state definitely his conviction in a popular lecture at Königsberg in 1840, and thereupon encouraged his talented assistant Flemming to begin reductions looking to its locating. Unfortunately, in the midst of his labors Flemming died, and shortly after Bessel himself, who had taken up the matter after Flemming's death.

"Somewhat later Arago, then head of the Paris observatory, who had also been impressed with the existence of such a planet, requested one of his assistants, a remarkable young mathematician named Leverrier, to undertake its investigation. Leverrier, who had already evidenced his marked ability in celestial mechanics, proceeded to grapple with the problem in the most thorough manner. He began by looking into the perturbations of Uranus by Jupiter and Saturn. He started with Bouvard's work, with the result of finding it very much the reverse of good. The farther he went, the more errors he found, until he was obliged to cast it aside entirely and recompute these perturbations himself. The catalogue of Bouvard's errors he gave must have been an eye-opener generally, and it speaks for the ability and precision with which Leverrier conducted his investigation that neither Airy, Bessel, nor Adams had detected these errors, with the exception of one term noticed by Bessel and subsequently by Adams.[2] The result of this recalculation of his was to show the more clearly that the irregularities in the

[2] Adams, "Explantion of the Motion of Uranus," 1846.

motion of Uranus could not be explained except by the existence of another planet exterior to him. He next set himself to locate this body. Influenced by Bode's law, he began by assuming it to lie at twice Uranus' distance from the Sun, and, expresssing the observed discrepancies in longitude in equations, comprising the perturbations and possible errors in the elments of Uranus, proceeded to solve them. He could get no rational solution. He then gave the distance and the extreme observations a certain elasticity, and by this means was able to find a position for the disturber which sufficiently satisfied the conditions of the problem. Leverrier's first memoir on the subject was presented to the French Academy on November 10, 1845, that giving the place of the disturbing planet on June 1, 1846. There is no evidence that the slightest search in consequence was made by anybody, with the possible exception of the Naval Observatory at Washington. On August 31 he presented his third paper, giving an orbit, mass, and more precise place for the unknown. Still no search followed. Taking advantage of the acknowledging of a memoir, Leverrier, in September, wrote to Dr. Galle in Berlin asking him to look for the planet. The letter reached Galle on the 23rd, and that very night he found a planet showing a disk just as Leverrier had foretold, and within 55' of its predicted place.

"The planet had scarcely been found when, on October 1, a letter from Sir John Herschel appeared in the *London Athenaeum* announcing that a young Cambridge graduate, Mr. J. C. Adams, had been engaged on the same investigation as Leverrier, and with similar results. This was the first public announcement of Mr. Adams' labors. It then appeared that he had started as early as 1843, and had communicated his results to Airy in October, 1845, a year before. Into the sad set of circumstances which prevented the brilliant young mathematician from reaping the fruit of what might have been his discovery, we need not go. It reflected no credit on any one concerned except Adams, who throughout his life maintained a dignified silence. Suffice it to say that Adams had found a place for the unknown within a few degrees of Leverrier's; that he had communicated these results to Airy; that Airy had not considered them significant until Leverrier had published an almost identical place; that then Challis, the head of the Cambridge Observatory, had set to work to search for the planet but so routinely that he had actually mapped it several times without finding that he had done so, when word arrived of its discovery by Galle.

"But now came an even more interesting chapter in this whole strange story. Mr. Walker at Washington and Dr. Petersen of Altona independently came to the conclusion from a provisional circular orbit for the newcomer that Lalande had catalogued in the vicinity of its path. They therefore set to work to find out if any Lalande stars were missing. Dr. Petersen compared a chart directly with the heavens to the finding a star absent, which his calculations showed was about where Neptune should have been at the time. Walker found that Lalande could only have swept in the neighborhood of Neptune on the 8th and 10th of May, 1795. By assuming different eccentricities for Neptune's orbit under two hypotheses for the place of its perihelion, he found a star catalogued on the latter date which sufficiently satisfied his computations. He predicted that on searching the sky this star would be found missing. On the next fine evening Professor Hubbard looked for it, and the star was gone. It had been Neptune.[3]

"This discovery enabled elliptic elements to be computed for it, when the surprising fact appeared that it was not moving in anything approaching the orbit either Leverrier or Adams had assigned. Instead of a mean distance of 36 astronomical units or more, the stranger was only at 30. The result so disconcerted Leverrier that he declared that 'the small eccentricity which appeared to result from Mr. Walker's computations would be incompatible with the nature of the perturbations of the planet Herschel,' as he called Uranus. In other words, he expressly denied that Neptune was his planet. For the newcomer proceeded to follow the path Walker had computed. This was strikingly confirmed by Mauvais' discovering that Lalande had observed the star on the 8th of May as well as on the 10th, but because the two places did not agree, he had rejected the first observation, and marked the second as doubtful, thus carefully avoiding a discovery that actually knocked at his door.

"Meanwhile Peirce had made a remarkable contribution to the whole subject. In a series of profound papers presented to the American Academy, he went into the matter more generally than either of the discoverers, to the startling conclusion 'that the planet Neptune is not the planet to which geometrical analysis had directed the telescope, and that its discovery by Galle must be regarded as a happy accident.'[4] He first proved this by showing that Leverrier's two fundamental propositions,—

[3] Proc. Amer. Acad., Vol. 1, p. 64.
[4] Proc. Amer. Acad., Vol. 1, p. 65 et seq.

"1. That the disturber's mean distance must be between 35 and 37.9 astronomical units;

"2. That its mean longitude for January 1, 1800, must have been between 243° and 252°,—

were incompatible with Neptune. Either alone might be reconciled with the observations, but not both.

"In justification of his assertion that the discovery was a happy accident, he showed that three solutions of the problem Leverrier had set himself were possible, all equally complete and decidedly different from each other, the positions of the supposed planet being 120° apart. Had Leverrier and Adams fallen upon either of the outer two, Neptune would not have been discovered.[5]

"He next showed that at 35.3 astronomical units, an important change takes place in the character of the perturbations because of the commensurability of period of a planet revolving there with that of Uranus. In consequence of which, a planet inside of this limit might equally account for the observed perturbations with the one outside of it supposed by Leverrier. This Neptune actually did. From not considering wide enough limits, Leverrier had found one solution, Neptune fulfilled the other.[6] And Bode's law was responsible for this. Had Bode's law not been taken originally as basis for the disturber's distance, those two great geometers, Leverrier and Adams, might have looked inside.

"This more general solution, as Peirce was careful to state, does not detract from the honor due either to Leverrier or to Adams. Their masterly calculations, the difficulty of which no one who has not had some experience of the subject can

[5] Proc. Amer. Acad., Vol. 1, p. 144.
[6] Proc. Amer. Acad., Vol. 1, p. 332.

appreciate, remain as an imperishable monument to both, as does also Peirce's to him."

The facts, that is what was done and written, are of course correct; but the conclusions drawn from them are highly controversial to the present day.

The calculations for finding an unknown planet by the perturbations it causes in the orbit of another are extremely difficult, the more so when the data are small and uncertain. For Percival they were very small because Neptune,—nearest to the unknown body,—had been discovered so short a time that its true orbit, apart from the disturbances therein caused by other planets, was by no means certain. In fact Percival tried to analyze its residuals, but they yielded no rational result. This left only what could be gleaned from Uranus after deducting the perturbations caused by Neptune, and that was small indeed. In 1845, when the calculations were made which revealed that planet, "the outstanding irregularities of Uranus had reached the relatively huge sum of 133″. To-day its residuals do not exceed 4.5″ at any point of its path."

Then there are uncertainties depending on errors of observation, which may be estimated by the method of least squares of the differences between contemporary observations. Moreover there is the uncertainty that comes from not knowing how much of the observed motion is to be attributed to a normal orbit regulated by the Sun, and how much to the other planets, including the unknown. Its true motion under these influences can be ascertained only by observing it for a long time, and by taking periods sufficiently far apart to distinguish the continuing effects of the known bodies from those that flow from an unknown source. This was the ingenious method devised by Leverrier as a basis for his calculations, and he thereby got his residuals caused by the unknown planet in a form that could be handled.

Finally there was the uncertainty whether the residual perturbations, however accurately determined, were caused by one or more outer bodies. Of this Percival was, of course, well aware, and in fact, in his study of the comets associated with Jupiter he had pointed out that there probably was a planet far beyond the one for which he was now in search. But, as no one has ever been able to devise a formula for the mutual attraction of three bodies, he could calculate only for a single body that would account as nearly as possible for the whole of the residuals.

Thus he knew that his work was an approximation; near enough, he hoped, to lead to the discovery of the unknown.

The various elements in the longitude of a planet's orbit, that is in the plane of the ecliptic, that are affected by and affect another, are:

a—The length of its major, or longest, axis.

n—Its mean motion, which depends on the distance from the Sun.

ϵ—The longitude at a given time, that is its place in its orbit.

e—The eccentricity of its orbit, that is how far it is from a circle.

$\bar{\omega}$—The place of its perihelion, that is the position of its nearest approach to the Sun.

(These last two determine the shape of the ellipse, and the direction of its longer axis with respect to that of the other planet.)

m—Its mass.

Now formulas, or series of equations, that express the perturbations caused by one planet in the orbit of another must contain all these elements, because all of them affect the result. But there are too many of them for a direct solution. Therefore Leverrier assumed a distance of the unknown planet from the Sun, and with it the mean motion which is proportional to that distance; worked out from the residuals of Uranus at various dates a series of equations in terms of the place of the unknown in its orbit; and then found what place therein at a given time would give results reducing the residuals to a minimum—that is, would come nearest to accounting for them. In fact, supposing that the unknown planet would be about the distance from the Sun indicated by Bode's law, the limits within which he assumed trial distances were narrow, and, as it proved, wholly beyond the place where it was found. This method, which in its general outline Percival followed, consisted therefore of a process of trial and error for the distance (with the mean motion) and for the place of X in its orbit (ϵ). For the other three elements (e, $\bar{\omega}$ and m) he used in the various solutions 24 to 37 equations drawn from the residuals of Uranus at different dates, and expressed in terms of ϵ. He did this in order to have several corroborative calculations, and to discover which of them accorded most closely with the perturbations observed.

We have seen that in 1908–09 Percival was inquiring about the exact residuals of Uranus, and he must have been at work on them soon afterwards, for on December 1, 1910, he writes to Mr. Lampland that Miss Williams, his head computer, and he have been puzzling away over that trans-Neptunian planet, have constructed the curve of perturbations, but find some strange things, looking as if Leverrier's later theory of Uranus were not exact. This work had been done by Leverrier's methods "but with extensions in the number and character of the terms calculated in the perturbation in order to render it more complete." Though uncertain of his results, he asks Mr. Lampland, in April 1911, to look for the planet. But he was by no means himself convinced that his data were accurate, and he computed all over again with the residuals given by Gaillot, which he considered more accurate than Leverrier's in regard to the masses, and therefore the attractions, of the known planets concerned. Incidentally he remarks at this point in his Memoir,[7] in speaking of works on celestial mechanics, that "after excellent analytical solutions, values of the quantities involved are introduced on the basis apparently of the respect due to age. Nautical Almanacs abet the practice by never publishing, consciously, contemporary values of astronomic constants; thus avoiding committal to doubtful results by the simple expedient of not printing anything not known to be wrong." His result for X, as he called the planet he was seeking, computed by Gaillot's residuals, differed from that found in using Leverrier's figures by some forty degrees to the East, and on July 8 he telegraphs Mr. Lampland to look there.

These telegrams to Mr. Lampland continue at short intervals for a long time with constant revisions and extensions in the calculations; and, as he notes, every new move takes weeks in the doing; but all without finding planet X. Perhaps it was this disappointment that led him to make the even more gigantic calculation printed in the Memoir, where

[7] Observatory "Memoir on a Trans-Neptunian Planet."

he says: "In the present case, it seemed advisable to pursue the subject in a different way, longer and more laborious than these earlier methods, but also more certain and exact: that by a true least-square method throughout. When this was done, a result substantially differing from the preliminary one was the outcome. It both shifted the minimum and bettered the solution. In consequence, the whole work was done *de novo* in this more rigorous way, with results which proved its value."

Then follow many pages of transformations which, as the guide books say of mountain climbing, no one should undertake unless he is sure of his feet and has a perfectly steady head. But anyone can see that, even in the same plane, the aggregate attractions of one planet on another, pulling eventually from all possible relative positions in their respective elliptical orbits with a force inversely as the square of the ever-changing distance, must form a highly complex problem. Nor, when for one of them the distance, velocity, mass, position and shape of orbit are wholly unknown, so that all these things must be represented by symbols, will anyone be surprised if the relations of the two bodies are expressed by lines of these, following one another by regiments over the pages. In fact the Memoir is printed for those who are thoroughly familiar with this kind of solitaire.

For the first trial and error Percival assumed the distance of X from the Sun to be 47.5 planetary units (the distance of the Earth from the Sun being the unit), as that seemed on analogy a probable, though by no means a certain, distance. With this as a basis, and with the actual observations of Uranus brought to the nearest accuracy by the method of least-squares of errors, he finds the eccentricity, the place of the perihelion and the mass of X in terms of its position in its orbit. Then he computes the results for about every ten degrees all the way round the orbit, and finds two positions, almost opposite, near 0° and near 180°, which reduce the residuals to a minimum—that is which most nearly account for the perturbations. Each of these thirty tried positions involved a vast amount of computation, but more still was to come.

Finally, to be sure that he had covered the ground and left no loophole for X to escape, he tried, beside the 47.5 he had already used, a series of other possible distances from the Sun,—40.5, 42.5, 45, 51.25 units,—each of them requiring every computation to be done over again. But the result was satisfactory, for it showed that the residuals were most nearly accounted for by a distance not far from 45 units (or a little less if the planet was at the opposite side of its orbit), and that the residuals increased for a distance greater or less than this. But still he was not satisfied, and for greater security he took up terms of the second and third order—very difficult to deal with—but found that they made no substanial difference in the result.

So much for the longitude of X (that is its orbit and position in the plane of the ecliptic) but that was not all, for its orbit might not lie in that plane but might be inclined to it, and like all the other planets he supposed it more or less so— more he surmised. Although he made some calculations on the subject he did not feel that any result obtained would be reliable, and if the longitude were near enough he thought the planet could be found. He says:

"To determine the inclination of the orbit of the unknown from the residuals in latitude of *Uranus* has proved as inconclusive as Leverrier found the like attempt in the case of *Neptune*.

"The cause of failure lies, it would seem, in the fact that the elements of X enter into the observational equations for the latitude. Not only e and $\bar{\omega}$ are thus initially affected but ϵ as well. Hence as these are doubtful from the longitude results, we can get from the latitude ones only doubtfulness to the second power." Nevertheless he makes some calculations on the subject which, however, prove unsatisfactory.

Such in outline was his method of calculating the probable orbit and position in the sky of the trans-Neptunian planet; an herculean labor carried out with infinite pains, and attaining, not absolute definiteness, but results from the varying solutions sufficiently alike to warrant the belief in a close approximation. In dealing with what he calls the credentials for the acceptance of his results, he points out that one of his solutions for X in which he has much confidence, reduces the squares of the residuals to be accounted for by ninety per cent., and in the case of some of the others almost to nothing. Yet he had no illusions about the uncertainty of the result, for in the conclusions of the Memoir he says:

"But that the investigation opens our eyes to the pitfalls of the past does not on that account render us blind to those of the present. To begin with, the curves of the solutions show that a proper change in the errors of observation would quite alter the minimum point for either the different mean distances or the mean longitudes. A slight increase of the actual errors over the most probable ones, such as it by no means strains human capacity for error to suppose, would suffice entirely to change the most probable distance of the

disturber and its longitude at the epoch. Indeed the impos-
ing 'probable error' of a set of observations imposes on no
one familiar with observation, the actual errors committed,
due to systematic causes, always far exceeding it.

"In the next place the solutions themselves tell us of alter-
natives between which they leave us in doubt to decide. If
we go by residuals alone, we should choose those solutions
which have their mean longitudes at the epoch in the neighborhood of 0°, since the residuals are there the smallest. But
on the other hand this would place the unknown now and
for many decades back in a part of the sky which has been
most assiduously scanned, while the solutions with ϵ around
180° lead us to one nearly inaccessible to most observatories,
and, therefore, preferable for planetary hiding. Between the
elements of the two, there is not much to choose, all agree-
ing pretty well with one another.

"Owing to the inexactitude of our data, then, we cannot
regard our results with the complacency of completeness
we should like."

The bulk of the computations for the trans-Neptunian
planet were finished by the spring of 1914, and in April he
sent to Flagstaff from Boston, where the work had been
done, two of the assistant computers. The final Memoir he
read to the American Academy of Arts and Sciences on
January 13, 1915; and printed in the spring as a publication
of the Observatory. Naturally he was deeply anxious to see
the fruit from such colossal labor. In July, 1913, he had
written to Mr. Lampland: "Generally speaking what fields
have you taken? Is there nothing suspicious?" and in
May, 1914, "Don't hesitate to startle me with a telegram
'FOUND.'" Again, in August, he writes to Dr. Slipher:

"I feel sadly of course that nothing has been reported about X, but I suppose the bad weather and Mrs. Lampland's condition may somewhat explain it"; and to Mr. Lampland in December: "I am giving my work before the Academy on January 13. It would be thoughtful of you to announce the actual discovery at the same time." Through the banter one can see the craving to find the long-sought planet, and the grief at the baffling of his hopes. That X was not found was the sharpest disappointment of his life.

If so much labor without tangible result gave little satisfaction, there was still less glory won by a vast calculation that did not prove itself correct. Curiously enough, he always enjoyed more recognition among astronomers in Europe than in America; for here, as a highly distinguished member of the craft recently remarked, he did not belong to the guild. He was fond of calling himself an amateur—by which he meant one who worked without remuneration—and of noting how many of the great contributors to science were in that category. The guild here was not readily hospitable to those who had not been trained in the regular treadmill; and it had been shocked by his audacity in proclaiming a discovery of intelligent handiwork on Mars. So for the most part he remained to the end of his life an amateur in this country; though what would have been said had he succeeded in producing, by rigorous calculation, an unknown planet far beyond the orbit of Neptune, it is interesting to conjecture, but difficult to know, for the younger generation of astronomers had not then come upon the stage nor the older ones outlived their prejudice.

The last eighteen months of his life were spent as usual partly at Flagstaff, where he was adding to the buildings,

partly in Boston, and in lecturing. In May, 1̶9̶ 93 ... an ...
to Sig. Rigano of "Scientia" that he has not time to wr...
article for his Review, and adds: "Eventually I hope to pub
lish a work on each planet—the whole connected together—
but the end not yet." Fortunately he did not know how
near it was.

In May he lectured at Toronto; and in the autumn in the
Northwest on Mars and other planets, at Washington State
and Reed Colleges, and the universities of Idaho, Washington, Oregon and California. These set forth his latest views,
often including much that had been discovered at Flagstaff
and elsewhere since his earlier books were published; for
his mind was far from closed to change of opinion on newly
discovered evidence. It was something of a triumphal pro-
cession at these institutions; but it was too much.

More exhausted than he was himself aware, he returned
to Flagstaff eager about a new investigation he had been
planning on Jupiter's satellites. It will be recalled that
he had found the exact position of the gap in Saturn's rings
accounted for if the inner layers of the planet rotated faster
and therefore were more oblate than the visible gaseous surface. Now the innermost satellite of Jupiter (the Vth) was
farther off than the simple relation between distance and
period should make it, a difference that might be explained
if in Jupiter, as in Saturn, the molten inner core were more
oblate than the outer gaseous envelope. To ascertain this
the distance of the satellite V. must be determined exactly,
and with Mr. E. C. Slipher he was busy in doing so night
after night through that of November 11th. But he was
overstrained, and the next day, November 12, 1916, not long
after his return to Flagstaff, an attack of apoplexy brought

...dden clo.... .s intens... ...ctive life. Before he became ...nscious he said that he always knew it would come ...us, but not so soon.

He lies buried in a mausoleum built by his widow close to the dome where his work was done.

CHAPTER XX

PLUTO FOUND [1]

PERCIVAL had long intended that his Observatory should be permanent, and that his work, especially on the planets, should be forever carried on there with an adequate foundation. Save for an income to his wife during her lifetime, he therefore left his whole fortune in a trust modeled on the lines of the Lowell Institute in Boston, created eighty years earlier by his kinsman John Lowell, Jr. The will provides for a single trustee who appoints his own successor; the first being his cousin Guy Lowell, the next the present trustee, Percival's nephew, Roger Lowell Putnam. Dr. V. M. Slipher and Mr. C. O. Lampland, who have been at the Observatory from an early time, are the astronomers in charge, carrying on the founder's principles of constantly enlarging the field of study, and using for the purpose the best instrumental equipment to be procured.

Of course the search was continued for the planet X, but without success, and for a time almost without hope, not only because its body is too small to show a disk, but also by reason of the multitude of stars of like size in that crowded part of the heavens, the Milky Way, where it is extremely

---

[1] Much of the following account is taken from "Searching Out Pluto" by Roger Lowell Putnam and Dr. V. M. Slipher in the *Scientific Monthly* for June, 1932, by whose courtesy it is used.

195

difficult to detect one that has moved. It was as if out of many thousand pins thrown upon the floor one were slightly moved and someone were asked to find which it was. Mere visual observation was clearly futile, for no man could record the positions of all the points of light from one night to another. The only way to conduct a systematic search was through an enduring record, that is by taking photographs of the probable sections of the sky, and comparing two of the same section taken a few days apart to discover a point of light that had changed its place—no simple matter when more than one hundred thousand stars showed upon a single plate. This process Percival tried, but although his hopes were often raised by finding bodies that moved, they proved to be asteroids hitherto unknown,[2] and the X sought so long did not appear.[3]

Percival had felt the need of a new photographic telescope of considerable light power and a wider field, and an attempt was made to borrow such an instrument, for use while one was being manufactured, but in vain. Then came the war when optical glass for large lenses could not be obtained, and before it was over Percival had died. After his death Guy Lowell, the trustee, took up the project, but also died too soon to carry it out. At last in 1929 the lens needed was obtained, the instrument completed in the workshop of the Observatory, and the search renewed in March with much better prospects. Photographs of section after section of the region where X was expected to be were taken and examined by a Blink comparator. This is a device whereby two photographs of slightly different dates could be seen through

[2] 515 asteroids and 700 variable stars were there disclosed.
[3] After X had been discovered two very weak images of it were found on photographic plates made in 1915—the year he published his Memoir.

a microscope at the same time as if superposed. But with all the improvement in apparatus months of labor revealed nothing.

After nearly a year of photographing, and comparing plates, Mr. Clyde W. Tombaugh, a young man brought up on a farm but with a natural love of astronomy, was working in this search at Flagstaff, when he suddenly found, on two plates taken January 23 and 29, 1930, a body that had moved in a way to indicate, not an asteroid, but something vastly farther off. It was followed, and appeared night after night in the path expected for X at about the distance from the sun Percival had predicted. Before giving out any information it was watched for seven weeks, until there could be no doubt from its movements that it was a planet far beyond Neptune, and was following very closely the track which his calculations had foretold. Then, on his birthday, March 13, the news was given to the world.

Recalling Percival's own statement: "Owing to the inexactitude of our data, then, we cannot regard our results with the complacency of completeness we should like," one inquires eagerly how nearly the actual elements in the orbit of the newly found planet agree with those he calculated. To this an answer was given by Professor Henry Norris Russell of Princeton, the leading astronomer in this country, in an article in the *Scientific American* for December, 1930. He wrote as follows:

"The orbit, now that we know it, is found to be so similar to that which Lowell predicted from his calculations fifteen years ago that it is quite incredible that the agreement can be due to accident. Setting prediction and fact side by side we have the following table of characteristics:

	Predicted	Actual
Period	282 years	249.17
Eccentricity	0.202	0.254
Longitude of perihelion	205°	202° 30'
Perihelion passage	1991.2	1989.16
Inclination	about 10°	17° 9'
Longitude of node	not predicted	109° 22'

"Lowell saw in advance that the perturbations of the latitudes of Uranus and Neptune (from which alone the position of the orbit plane of the unknown planet could be calculated) were too small to give a reliable result and contented himself with the prophecy that the inclination, like the eccentricity, would be considerable. For the other four independent elements of the orbit, which are those that Lowell actually undertook to determine by his calculations, the agreement is good in all cases, the greatest discrepancy being in the period, which is notoriously difficult to determine by computations of this sort. In view of Lowell's explicit statement that since the perturbations were small the resulting elements of the orbit could at best be rather rough approximations, the actual accordance is all that could be demanded by a severe critic.

"Even so, the table does not tell the whole story. Figure 1 [4] shows the actual and the predicted orbits, the real positions of the planet at intervals from 1781 to 1989, and the positions resulting from Lowell's calculations. It appears at once that the predicted positions of the orbit and of the planet upon it were nearest right during the 19th century and the early part

[4] This figure slightly changed for later observations is on the opposite page.

of the 20th, while at earlier and later dates the error rapidly increased. Now this (speaking broadly) is just the interval covered by the observations from which the influence of the planet's attraction could be determined and, therefore, the

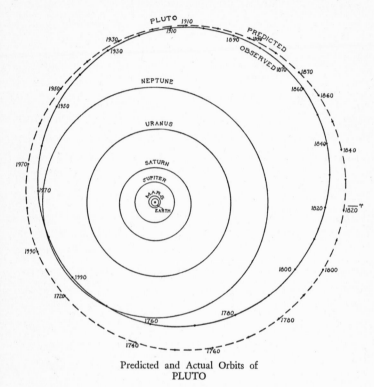

Predicted and Actual Orbits of
PLUTO

interval in which calculation could find the position of the planet itself with the least uncertainty.

"In the writer's judgment this test is conclusive." [5]

[5] Dr. A. C. D. Crommelin, the highest authority in England on such matters, had expressed the same conclusion; and the Royal Astronomical Society had cabled its felicitations on the discovery. Professor Russell's latest views may be found in Appendix 1. *infra*.

Later observations, and computations of the orbit of Pluto, do not vary very much from those that Professor Russell had when he wrote. Two of the most typical—giving more elements—are as follows:

	Predicted	Nicholson and Mayall	F. Zagar
Period	282 years	249.2	248.9
Eccentrictiy	0.202	0.2461	0.2472
Longitude of perihelion	204.9	222° 23′ 20″.17	222° 29′ 39″.4
Perihelion passage	1991.2	1889.75	1888.4
Inclination	about 10°	17° 6′ 58″.4	17° 6′ 50″.8
Semi-major axis	43.	39.60	39.58
Perihelion distance	34.31	29.86	29.80
Aphelion distance	51.69	49.35	49.36

Except for the eccentricity, and the inclination which he declared it impossible to calculate, these results have proved as near as, with the uncertainty of his data, he could have expected; and in regard to the position of the planet in its orbit it will be recalled that he found two solutions on opposite sides, both of which would account almost wholly for the residuals of Uranus. The one that came nearest to doing so he had regarded as the least probable because it placed the planet in a part of the sky that had been much searched without finding it; but it was there that Pluto appeared—a striking proof of his rigorous analytic method.

But the question of its mass has raised serious doubts whether Pluto can have caused the perturbations of Uranus from which he predicted its presence, for if it has no significant mass the whole basis of the calculation falls to the ground, and there has been found a body travelling, by a marvellous coincidence, in such an orbit that, if large enough, it would produce the perturbations but does not do so.[6] Now as there is no visible satellite to gauge its attraction, and as it will be long before Pluto in its eccentric orbit approaches Neptune or Uranus closely enough to measure accurately by that means, the mass cannot yet be determined with certainty. What is needed are measures of position of the highest possible accuracy of Neptune and Uranus, long continued and homogeneous.

The reasons for the doubt about adequate mass are two.[7] One that with the largest telescopes it shows no visible disk, and must therefore be very small in size, and hence in mass unless its density is much greater, or its albedo far less, than those of any other known planet. The other substantially that the orbits of Uranus and Neptune can be, and are more naturally, explained by assuming appropriate elements therefor, without the intervention of Pluto's disturbing force. This is precisely what Percival stated in discussing the correctness of the residuals—that it was always possible to account for the motions of a planet, whose normal orbit about the sun is not definitely ascertained, by throwing any observed divergencies either on errors in the supposed orbit, or upon perturbations by an unknown body.

The conditions here are quite unlike those at the discovery of Neptune, for there the existence of the perturba-

---

[6] The non-expert reader must remember that the mass and the size—still more the apparent size—are very different things, and the mass is the only one that could be found by calculation, for this alone affects the attraction, which at such a distance is quite independent of the density and hence of the size. Moreover, the apparent size depends also upon the extent to which the surface reflects the light of the sun—technically termed the planet's albedo—a matter that has no relation to the perturbation of another body.

[7] "The Astronomical Romance of Pluto"—Professor A. O. Leuschner—Publications of *The Astronomical Society of the Pacific*, August, 1932.

tions was clear, because fairly large, and the orbit predicted was wrong because of an error in the distance assumed; and the question was whether the presence of Neptune in the direction predicted, though in a different orbit, was an accident, or inevitable. Here the predicted orbit is substantially the actual one, adequate to account for the perturbations of Uranus if such really exist, and the question is whether they do or not. If not the discovery of Pluto is a mere unexplained coincidence which has no connection with the prediction. Whether among recognized uncertainties it is more rational to suppose a very high density, and very low albedo, with corresponding perturbations of Uranus and Neptune, whose orbits are still imperfectly known, or to conclude that a planet, which would account for these things if dense enough, revolves in fact in the appropriate path, a mere ghost of itself—a phantom but not a force—one who is not an astronomer must leave to the professionals.

In the case of both Neptune and Pluto the calculation was certainly a marvellous mathematical feat, and in accord with the usual practice whereby the discoverer of a new celestial body is entitled to propose its name the observers at Flagstaff selected from many suggestions that of "Pluto" with the symbol ♇; and henceforth astronomers will be reminded of Percival Lowell, by the planet he found but never saw.

APPENDIX I

Professor Henry Norris Russell's later views on the size of Pluto (written to the Biographer and printed with the writer's consent).

LATER investigations have revealed a very curious situation. When once the elements of Pluto's orbit are known, the calculation of the perturbations which it produces on another planet, such as Neptune, are greatly simplified. But the problem of finding Pluto's mass from observations of Neptune is still none too easy, for the perturbations affect the calculated values of the elements of Neptune's orbit, and are thus "entangled" with them in an intricate fashion.

Nicholson and Mayall, in 1930, attacked the problem, and found that the perturbations of Neptune by Pluto, throughout the interval from its discovery to the present, were almost exactly similar to the effects which would have been produced by certain small changes in the elements of Neptune's orbit, so that, from these observations alone, it would have been quite impossible to detect Pluto's influence. Outside this interval of time, the effects of the perturbations steadily diverge from those of the spurious changes in the orbit, but we cannot go into the future to observe them, and all we have in the past is two rather inaccurate observations made in 1795 by Lalande.[1] If the average of these two discordant observations is taken as it stands, Pluto's mass comes out 0.9 times that of the Earth, and this determination is entitled to very little weight.

Uranus is farther from Pluto, and its perturbations are smaller; but it has been accurately observed over one and a half revolutions, as against half a revolution for Neptune, and this greatly favors the separation of the perturbations from changes in the assumed orbital elements. Professor E. W. Brown—the most distinguished living student of the subject—concludes from a

[1] See page 181 *supra*.

careful investigation that the observations of Uranus show that
Pluto's mass cannot exceed one-half of the Earth's and may be
much less. In his latest work a great part of the complication
is removed by a curiously simple device. Take the sum of the
residuals of Uranus at any two dates separated by one-third of
its period, and subtract from this the residual at the middle date.
Brown proves—very simply—that the troublesome effect of uncertainties in the eccentricity and perihelion of the disturbed
planet will be completely removed from the resulting series of
numbers, leaving the perturbations much easier to detect. The
curve which expresses their effects, though changed in shape, can
easily be calculated. Applying this method to the longitude of
Uranus, he finds, beside the casual errors of observation, certain
deviations; but these change far more rapidly than perturbations
due to Pluto could possibly do, and presumably arise from small
errors in calculating the perturbations produced by Neptune.
When these are accurately re-calculated, a minute effect of
Pluto's attraction may perhaps be revealed, but Brown concludes
that "another century of accurate observations appears to be necessary for a determination which shall have a probable error
less than a quarter of the Earth's mass."

The conclusion that Pluto's mass is small is confirmed by its
brightness. Its visual magnitude is 14.9—just equal to that which
Neptune's satellite Triton would have if brought to the same
distance. (Since Pluto's perihelion distance is less than that of
Neptune, this experiment is one which Nature actually performs
at times.) Now Nicholson's observations show that the mass of
Triton is between 0.06 and 0.09 times the Earth's. It is highly
probable that Pluto's mass is about the same—in which case
the perturbations which it produces, even on Neptune, will be
barely perceptible, so long as observations have their present
degree of accuracy.

The value of seven times the Earth's mass, derived in Percival
Lowell's earlier calculations, must have been influenced by some
error. His mathematical methods were completely sound—on
Professor Brown's excellent authority—and the orbit of Planet X
which he computed resembled so closely that of the actual Pluto
that no serious discordance could arise from the difference. But,
in this case also, the result obtained for the mass of the perturbing planet depended essentially on the few early observa-

tions of Uranus as a star, made before its discovery as a planet, and long before the introduction of modern methods of precise observation. Errors in these are solely responsible for the inaccuracy in the results of the analytical solution.

The question arises, if Percival Lowell's results were vitiated in this way by errors made by others more than a century before his birth, why is there an actual planet moving in an orbit which is so uncannily like the one he predicted?

There seems no escape from the conclusion that this is a matter of chance. That so close a set of chance coincidences should occur is almost incredible, but the evidence assembled by Brown permits of no other conclusion. Other equally remarkable coincidences have occurred in scientific experience. A cipher cablegram transmitting to the Lick Observatory the place of a comet discovered in Europe was garbled in transmission, and when decoded gave an erroneous position in the heavens. Close to this position that evening another undiscovered comet was found. More recently a slight discrepancy between determinations of the atomic weight of hydrogen by the mass-spectrograph and by chemical means led to a successful search for a heavy isotope of hydrogen. Later and more precise work with the mass-spectrograph showed that the discrepancy had at first been much overestimated. Had this error not been made, heavy hydrogen might not yet have been discovered.

Like this later error, the inaccuracy in the ancient observations, which led to an over-estimate of the mass and brightness of Pluto, was a fortunate one for science.

In any event, the initial credit for the discovery of Pluto justly belongs to Percival Lowell. His analytical methods were sound; his profound enthusiasm stimulated the search, and, even after his death, was the inspiration of the campaign which resulted in its discovery at the Observatory which he had founded.

APPENDIX II

THE LOWELL OBSERVATORY

by Professor Henry Norris Russell

THE Observatory at Flagstaff is Percival Lowell's creation. The material support which he gave it, both during his lifetime and by endowment, represents but a small part of his connection with it. He chose the site, which in its combination of excellent observing conditions and the amenities of everyday life, is still unsurpassed. He selected the permanent members of the staff and provided for the successor to the Directorship after his death. Last, but not least, he inspired a tradition of intense interest in the problems of the universe, and independent and original thought in attacking them, which survives unimpaired.

On a numerical basis—whether in number of staff, size of instruments, or annual budget—the Lowell Observatory takes a fairly modest rank in comparison with some great American foundations. But throughout its history it has produced a long and brilliant series of important discoveries and observations notable especially for originality of conception and technical skill. Percival Lowell's own work has been fully described; it remains to summarize briefly that of the men whom he chose as his colleagues, presenting it according to its subject, rather than in chronological order.

The photography of the planets has been pursued for thirty years, mainly by the assiduous work of E. C. Slipher, and the resulting collections are unrivalled. Only a small amount of this store has been published or described in print, but among its successes may be noted the first photographs of the canals of Mars, and the demonstration by this impersonal method of the seasonal changes in the dark areas, and of the occasional appearance of clouds. It is a commonplace that any astronomer who wants photographs of the planets for any illustrative purpose instinctively applies to his friends in Flagstaff, and is not likely to be disappointed.

The discovery of Pluto, and incidentally of many hundreds of asteroids, has already been described.

An important series of measurements of the radiation from the planets was made at Flagstaff in 1921 and 1922 by Dr. W. W. Coblentz of the Bureau of Standards and Dr. C. O. Lampland. Using the 40-inch reflector, and the vacuum thermocouples which the former had developed, and employed in measurements of stellar radiation at the Lick Observatory, and working with and without a water-cell (which transmits most of the heat carried by the sunlight reflected from a planet, but stops practically all of that radiated from its own surface), they found that the true "planetary heat" from Jupiter was so small that its surface must be very cold, probably below — 100° Centigrade, while that from Mars was considerable, indicating a relatively high temperature. Both conclusions have been fully confirmed by later work.

Spectroscopic observation has been equally successful. In 1912 Lowell and Slipher (V. M.) successfully attacked the difficult problem of the rotation of Uranus. One side of a rotating planet is approaching us, the other receding. If its image is thrown on a spectroscope, so that its equatorial regions fall upon the slit, the lines of the spectrum will be shifted toward the violet on one edge, and the red on the other, and will cross it at a slant instead of at right angles. This method had long before been applied to Jupiter and to Saturn and its rings, but Uranus is so faint as to discourage previous observation. Nevertheless, with the 24-inch reflector, and a single-prism spectrograph, seven satisfactory plates were obtained, with an average exposure of $2\frac{1}{2}$ hours, every one of which showed a definite rotation effect. The mean result indicated that Uranus rotates in $10\frac{3}{4}$ hours, with motion retrograde, as in the case of his satellites. This result was confirmed five years later by Leon Campbell at Harvard, who observed regular variations in the planet's brightness with substantially the same period.

It has been known since the early days of the spectroscope that the major planets exhibit in their spectra bands produced by absorption by the gases of their atmospheres, and that these bands are strongest in the outer planets. Photographs showing this were first made by V. M. Slipher at the Lowell Observatory in 1902. To get adequate spectrograms of Neptune required exposures of 14 and 21 hours—occupying the available parts of the clear nights of a week. The results well repaid the effort. The bands which appear faintly in Jupiter are very strong in Uranus, and enormous in Neptune's spectrum, cutting out great portions of the red and yellow, and accounting for the well-known greenish color of the planet. Only one band in the red was present in Jupiter alone.

For a quarter of a century after this discovery those bands remained one of the most perplexing riddles of astrophysics. The conviction gradually grew that they must be due to some familiar gases, but the first hint of their origin was obtained by Wildt in 1932, who showed that one band in Jupiter was produced by ammonia gas, and another probably by methane. These conclusions were confirmed by Dunham in the following year, but the general solution of the problem was reserved for Slipher and Adel, who, in 1934, announced that the whole series of unidentified bands were due to methane. The reason why they had not been identified sooner is that it requires an enormous thickness of gas to produce them. A tube 45 meters long, containing methane at 40 atmospheres pressure, produces bands comparable to those in the spectra of Saturn. The far heavier bands in Neptune indicate an atmosphere equivalent to a layer 25 miles thick at standard atmospheric pressure. The fainter bands though not yet observed in the laboratory, have been conclusively identified by the theory of band-spectra. Ammonia shows only in Jupiter and faintly in Saturn; the gas is doubtless liquefied or solidified at the very low temperatures of the outer planets.

The earth's own atmosphere has also been the subject of discovery at Flagstaff. The light of a clear moonless sky does not come entirely from the stars and planets; about one-third of it originates in the upper air, and shows a spectrum of bright lines and bands. The familiar auroral line is the most conspicuous of these, but V. M. Slipher, making long exposures with instruments of remarkably great light-gathering power, has recently detected a large number of other bands, in the deep red and even the infra-red. Were our eyes strongly sensitive to these wave-lengths, the midnight skies would appear ruddy.

Just as the first rays of the rising sun strike the upper layers of the atmosphere many miles above the surface, new emission bands appear in the spectrum—to be drowned out soon afterwards by the twilight reflected from the lower and denser layers; and the reverse process is observable after sunset.

The origin of these remarkable and wholly unexpected radiations is not yet determined.

The spectrograph of the Observatory was also employed in observations of stars, and again led to unexpected discoveries. In 1908, while observing the spectroscopic binary Beta Scorpii, V. M. Slipher found that the K line of calcium was sharp on his plates, while all the others were broad and diffuse. Moreover, while the broad lines shifted in position as the bright star moved in its orbit, the narrow line remained stationery. Hartmann, in 1904, had observed a similar line in the spectra of Delta Orionis, and suggested that it was absorbed in a cloud of gas somewhere between the sun and the star. Slipher, extending his observations to other parts of the heavens, found that such stationery calcium lines were very generally present (in spectra of such types that they were not masked by heavier lines arising in the stars themselves), and made the bold suggestion that the absorbing medium was a "general veil" of gas occupying large volumes of interstellar space.

This hypothesis, which appeared hardly credible at that time, has been abundantly confirmed—both by the discovery of similar stationery lines of sodium, and by the theoretical researches of Eddington,—and no one now doubts that interstellar space is thinly populated by isolated metallic atoms presumably ejected from some star in the remote past, but now wandering in the outer darkness, with practically no chance of returning to the stars.

To secure satisfactory spectroscopic observations of nebulae is often very difficult. Though some of these objects are of considerable brightness, they appear as extended luminous surfaces in the heavens, and in the focal plane of the telescope. The slit of a spectroscope, which must necessarily be narrow to permit good resolution of the lines, admits but a beggarly fraction of the nebula's light. To increase the size of the telescope helps very little, for, though more light is collected in the nebular image, this image is proportionately increased in area, and no more light enters the slit than before.

For the gaseous nebulae, whose spectra consist of separate bright lines, there is no serious difficulty; but the majority of nebulae have continuous spectra, and when the small amount of light that traverses the slit is spread out into a continuous band, it becomes so faint that prohibitively long exposures would be required to photograph it. It was at the Lowell Observatory that Dr. V. M. Slipher first devised a way of meeting this difficulty.

By employing in the camera of the spectrograph (which forms the image of the spectrum on the plate) a lens of short focus, this image became both shorter and narrower, thereby increasing the intensity of the light falling on a given point of the plate in a duplicate ratio. Moreover, since with this device the image of the slit upon the plate is much narrower than the slit itself, it became possible to open the slit more widely and admit much more of the light of the nebula, without spoiling the definition of the spectral lines.

This simple but ingenious artifice opened up a wholly new field of observation, and led to discoveries of great importance.

Within the cluster of the Pleiades, and surrounding it, are faint streaky wisps of nebulosity, which have long been known. One might have guessed that the spectrum, like that of some other filamentous nebulae, would be gaseous. But when Slipher photographed it in December 1912 (with an exposure of 21 hours, on three successive nights) he found a definite continuous spectrum, crossed by strong dark lines of hydrogen and fainter lines of helium—quite unlike the spectrum of any previously observed nebula, but "a true copy of that of the brighter stars in the Pleiades." Careful auxiliary studies showed that the light which produced this spectrum came actually from the nebula. This suggested at once that this nebula is not self-luminous, but shines by the reflected light of the stars close to it. This conclusion has been fully verified by later observations, at Flagstaff and elsewhere. It is only under favorable conditions that one of these vast clouds (probably of thinly scattered dust) lies near enough to any star to be visibly illuminated. The rest reveal themselves as dark markings against the background of the Milky Way.

Similar observations of the Great Nebula of Orion showed that the conspicuous "nebular" lines found in its brighter portions faded out in its outer portions, leaving the hydrogen lines bright, while, at the extreme edge, only a faint continuous spectrum appeared. This again has been fully explained by Bowen's discovery of the mechanism of excitation of nebular radiation by the ultra-violet light from exceedingly hot stars, and affords a further confirmation of it.

But the most important contribution of the new technique was in the observation of the spiral nebulae. Their spectra are continuous and so faint that previous instruments brought out only tantalizing suggestions of dark lines. With the new spectrograph, beautiful spectra were obtained, showing numerous dark lines, of just the character that might have been expected from vast clouds of stars of all spectral types. This provided the first definite indication of one of the greatest of modern astronomical discoveries—that the white nebulae are external galaxies, of enormous dimensions, and at distances beyond the dreams of an earlier generation.

By employing higher dispersion, spectra were secured which permitted the measurement of radial velocity. The first plates, of the Andromeda Nebula, revealed the almost unprecedented speed of 300 kilometers per second toward the Sun. Later measures of many other nebulae showed that this motion was, for a nebula, unusually slow, but remarkable in its direction, for practically all the others were receding.

Similar measures upon globular star-clusters showed systematic differences in various parts of the heavens, which indicated that, compared with the vast system of these clusters, the Sun is moving at the rate of nearly 300 kilometers per second— a motion which is now attributed to its revolution, in a vast orbit, about the center of the Galaxy, as a part of the general rotation of the latter.

The velocities of the nebulae reveal substantially the same solar motion, but, over and above this, an enormous velocity of recession, increasing with the faintness and probable distance of the nebulae.

This, again, was a discovery of primary importance. It has

been confirmed at other observatories and observations with the largest existing telescope have revealed still greater velocities of recession in nebulae too faint to observe at Flagstaff. How this has led to the belief that the material universe is steadily expanding and that its ascertainable past history covers only some two thousand millions of years, can only be mentioned here.

This is a most remarkable record for thirty years' work of a single observatory with a regular staff never exceeding four astronomers. But its distinction lies less in the amount of the work than in its originality and its fertile character in provoking extensive and successful researches at other observatories as well.

All this is quite in the spirit of its Founder, and, to his colleagues in the science, makes the Observatory itself seem his true monument. His body lies at rest upon the hill, but, in an unquenched spirit of eager investigation, his soul goes marching on.